Kids SPEAK 12

chaim walder

Translated by
Aviva Rappaport

Illustrated by
Devorah Benedict

FELDHEIM PUBLISHERS

Originally published in 2020 in Hebrew as
Yeladim Mesaprim al Atzmam (Vol. 12)

First published 2020
ISBN 978-1-68025-437-2

Translated by Aviva Rappaport
Illustrated by Devorah Benedict

Feldheim Publishers
POB 43163 / Jerusalem, Israel

208 Airport Executive Park
Nanuet, NY 10954

www.feldheim.com

DISTRIBUTED IN EUROPE BY:
Lehmanns
+44-0-191-430-0333
info@lehmanns.co.uk
www.lehmanns.co.uk

DISTRIBUTED IN AUSTRALIA BY:
Golds World of Judaica
+613 95278775
info@golds.com.au
www.golds.com.au

Printed in Israel

To Itamar and Yaeli!
My precious, beloved grandchildren!
May you continue the life story of my son,
my firstborn, Tzviki, *z"l*

_____

Contents

Between Man and Hashem

My name is Orit.

My story took place when I was twelve years old, at my sixth-grade graduation party. Mothers were invited as were all the teachers in our school. My friends and I were excited about performing in front of all our mothers.

Because my grandfather had passed away that year, my mother was still in the year of mourning and couldn't attend. She asked my grandmother to go in her place.

My grandmother is a Holocaust survivor who emigrated from Hungary to the United States after the war. She married my grandfather (who saved her from death at Auschwitz when he pulled her from the line headed to the "showers" and pointed her in the direction of work. But that's a story of its own.) They made their home in New Jersey, where their two daughters were born. My mother was one of them.

My mother suffered a lot of antisemitism at the school she attended, so when she was fourteen, she decided to go to school in Eretz Yisrael. She went to live with an aunt and attended school in Kfar Pines. Four years later, her parents came too, and the family was reunited and made their home in Petach Tikvah.

*   *   *

That night, my grandmother and I went to the graduation party together. The seating in the auditorium was arranged so that one side had chairs and the other side had rows of bleachers. My grandmother, an elderly woman, went to sit on one of the chairs, and I accompanied her to her seat.

A few minutes later, as we waited for the performance to start, a teacher came over to my grandmother and told her that she was sitting on the side reserved for teachers. "Over there—" she pointed across the aisle "—is where the mothers are supposed to sit."

My grandmother got the message loud and clear. I wasn't the only one watching the scene, either. My friends were also watching as the teacher told an elderly woman to get up from her seat, and they all recognized that elderly woman as my grandmother.

I remember how embarrassed I felt for my grand-mother, for the person who told her to move from where she was sitting, and for myself as well. Because when someone embarrasses your grandmother in pub-lic, they're embarrassing you, too.

At first, my grandmother sat there numbly, not moving. All of a sudden, she stood up and pulled up her sleeve, revealing the Auschwitz number tattooed on her arm.

"Do you know who the last person was who told me to go to the other side?" she said to the teacher.

A hush fell over the auditorium, and everyone heard what she was saying. The shocked teacher didn't answer.

My grandmother turned around and left to go home, while I, a twelve-year-old girl, stood there speechless.

Right then, the announcement came to go up on stage. The show must go on.

I don't know why I didn't run after my grandmoth-er. I think I was just sort of numb. I knew her story. Maybe not everything, but enough to understand the meaning of what she'd said.

My grandmother suffered a lot in the Holocaust. She lost her whole family and stood face to face with

the evil Nazi Josef Mengele, *ym"s*. Standing there in front of him when he pointed, she'd felt humiliated. The humiliation she'd just experienced took her back to those terrible times. With good reason Chazal tell us that shaming or embarrassing another person in public is like spilling their blood.

*   *   *

The rest of the evening passed before my eyes in a dark blur until my mother finally came. I spotted her sitting on a bleacher in the section reserved for mothers.

The party continued, and in the album there's a picture of me receiving my report card and a siddur, and another one of my mother and me. I'm standing there frozen, without a smile. A much worse picture was engraved on my heart.

I never talked about what happened, neither to my mother nor to my grandmother. I was too embarrassed to talk to my grandmother about her public humiliation. As for my mother, I didn't talk to her because I also felt humiliated, and I guess I was ashamed to talk about it.

Today I know that my silence wasn't good, because the humiliation and pain stayed inside me. But that's how I decided to act, I'm sorry to say.

A few years have passed since then. You're probably wondering how many. Now I'll surprise you: thirty years have gone by.

*   *   *

Sorry if you thought a twelve-year-old girl was telling you this story, but that's what I wanted you to think. I wanted to tell the story through a young girl's eyes, and then, through a woman's eyes.

When I grew up, I married and became a mother as well as a teacher. In the classroom, whenever one student sat in another student's seat, the first student would ask me to make the other girl move. I'd get very tense and reprimand the student who'd asked me to make the other student move.

"Never tell someone who's sitting in your seat to move. You be the one to find a different seat."

I'm so sensitive to this issue that whenever I saw a scene like that starting, I'd step in to make sure it didn't happen, that no girl would dare make someone who'd taken her seat give it up. I myself would stand up immediately whenever anyone came close to where I was sitting, always worried that perhaps I'd taken her seat. I didn't want a repeat of my grandmother's situation, where they made her get up. It goes without saying that I never, ever asked someone who mistakenly took my seat to move.

I hadn't thought about this incident at my sixth-grade graduation until three years ago, and I'm not sure why I did then. Maybe it was because a student asked me, "Why can't I say something? It's my seat. Why can't I tell her to get up?" I remembered the story, and I couldn't stop crying. Thirty years of pent-up fury at that teacher who'd dared to tell my grandmother to move burst out from inside me. Why hadn't she understood that you just don't do something like that?

Erev Yom Kippur I told my class the story and cried again. I talked about a mistake a teacher can make and how it can affect a student's whole life.

"I'm asking two things of you," I told the girls. "One is, don't make anyone get up from where they're sitting even if it was your seat. They must have sat there by mistake. Not only does asking them to move show poor *middos*, but it can hurt their feelings badly. And two, please tell me when I make a mistake so that I can correct it on the spot. I don't want any of you to ever carry a scar with you for life."

A year ago, I was at a Playback Theater show, in which the performers act out real stories from the audience. I decided to go up on stage with my story. It still bothered me and it still hurt—which made me think I hadn't fully resolved my feelings about it.

After I told my story, the emcee asked me if I'd forgiven the teacher—and if I hadn't, if I wanted to.

She acted out the teacher as a person who made an unintentional mistake, and asked my forgiveness. I cried like I hadn't cried in years. I guess the heaviness of it all, the anger I'd never let go of, had been weighing me down more than I'd realized.

Afterward, I went over to my mother and asked her if she remembered what had happened that night. I had to remind her what I was talking about, but then she told me that after the graduation performance she went over to the teacher and told her what had happened. The teacher had immediately called my grandmother to apologize.

Too bad I didn't see that. All those years, and I hadn't known.

* * *

Now my family and students know the full story, to which I've added a few important points.

Kids who feel that someone's hurt either them or someone close to them need to talk to an adult about what happened. If such a conversation had taken place between the teacher and me, if the issue had been resolved, the hurt feelings wouldn't have stayed with me for so many years.

It's so important to forgive. We experience so much emotional pain when we carry around past hurts and humiliations. Forgiving is important not only to the one who hurt someone but also to the one who felt hurt.

I think this story is about understanding the other person. For instance, if a girl interrupts a conversation between two of her friends, it can be annoying. Some girls will even say to her, "Don't you see that we're in the middle of a conversation?" But nothing will happen if their conversation is put off for a different time. It's not only a *chesed*, but it will spare someone from humiliation.

This story has a happy ending. I've internalized my personal experience and drawn from it these important life messages. The Playback people gave my story the name *"Bein Adam LaMakom*—Between Man and Hashem." I don't think there's anything more important than "HaMakom." Hidden are His ways of teaching us about our "place" (*makom*) in the world and the consideration we should have for the place of others.

Birkas Kohanim

My name is Etty.

I'm twelve, and I live in northern Israel.

My story, which took place three years ago, is proof that we don't always know what's best for us. We can always say, "*Gam zu l'tovah*, this too is for the best," and strengthen our *emunah*.

It all began on a flight to the States for my cousin's bar mitzvah. My mother didn't make the trip because she'd just had a baby, and she needed to stay home with her and the other little kids. We were going for a five-day visit, during which we'd get together with our extended family in America.

On Shabbos, my bar mitzvah cousin got an *aliyah*, and it was exciting to see all our relatives. I still felt a little jet-lagged. My head was also spinning from trying to remember the names and faces of all the relatives.

Our flight home was supposed to leave on Sunday at 1:30 a.m. Little did we know what was in store for us.

We packed and then went to sleep until Abba woke us at eleven. My *savta* drove us to the airport, which was near her house. At the airport, we went through all the security checks. Once all our bags were checked, including the new stroller we'd bought for the baby, we prepared to board.

Suddenly, we ran into a friend of my father's, who said he was on the same flight.

"You're a *kohen*, aren't you?" he said to my father.

"Yes, I am," my father said, looking surprised.

"It's like this," his friend said. "I saw one of the passengers holding a booklet on the laws of *aveilus*."

"I see," my father said.

My father saw, but we didn't.

* * *

Abba took a seat and explained that sometimes people who die abroad wanted to be buried in Eretz Yisrael. The coffin is put in the plane's cargo hold and flown to Eretz Yisrael. There, it's removed, and they make a *levayah*.

"As soon as a coffin is placed aboard a plane, *kohanim* cannot be on that plane," my father explained.

He walked quickly to the chief flight attendant and asked, "Is there a body on board the plane being brought for burial?"

"Yes," the man said.

Abba quickly called our Rav, apologized for the late hour, and asked him what he should do. The Rav said that it's forbidden for a *kohen* to board the plane. As soon as my father told us this, I started to cry. I was sure we'd have to stay in the States for another week or two, and I was already homesick.

My father calmed me down by explaining that there are several flights a day to Israel, so there was nothing to worry about. We would probably be able to board the next flight.

Everything I just told you happened before 1:00 a.m.

By now, we were practically falling asleep on our feet. As soon as my father knew we wouldn't be boarding the flight, he notified to the flight attendant. It wasn't easy, because first he had to explain what it meant to be a *kohen*. It took them a while to get it because it was a non-Jewish airline. By law, baggage cannot go on a flight unless its owner is a passenger, so they had to delay the plane's takeoff to remove our baggage.

They didn't find the stroller and informed us that

it would go on the flight without us. If it turned up in Israel, they'd notify us.

We stood there, tired and dazed, watching our plane take off without us. I started crying again. Picture it: it's the middle of the night, we're far from home, we'd already imagined flying back and seeing Ima, and now we were stuck in the airport with no idea when the next flight would be.

We ordered a taxi to take us back to our *savta's* house. It was a bumpy ride, and I threw up. We got there at around four in the morning. Savta couldn't believe we were back. She'd thought we were high in the sky on our way home. We told her what had happened and went to sleep.

My father couldn't fall asleep; he was too worried about finding another flight quickly. In the morning, he davened with a *vasikin* minyan and started calling travel agents. It turned out that all the flights were full. Finally, after dozens of phone calls—and lots of *tehillim* on our part—he found a flight leaving from a more distant airport at one thirty that afternoon.

The only thing was, boarding closed at twelve thirty and the airport was an hour's drive from Savta's house. We gathered our things and decided to try to make that flight. My father ordered a taxi, and we all jumped in.

*   *   *

It was a stressful ride. The driver was very laid-back, which had the opposite effect on us. My father told him that it didn't look like he was following the GPS, which showed the quickest route, to which the driver replied casually that he didn't believe in it.

I looked at my father. He was usually a calm person, but now I saw he was stressed and with good reason. We were in a hurry, but the driver didn't believe in technology! All of a sudden, my father said, "You know what? We also don't believe in technology, only in G-d. We'll pray, and everything will be okay."

The driver's sense of direction turned out to be good because we arrived at the airport at twelve fifteen. We had fifteen minutes to get through baggage checks and security. Abba tried to do everything quickly, and we actually did get through all the checks fast. But then we couldn't find my passport. Abba had to run back to the check-in counter we were at before and tell them that we gave them four passports but they only gave us back three.

"We don't have a passport here," the agent said.

Then we experienced *siyatta diShemaya* once again:

a cleaner who was working nearby came over to my father, pointed to his dustpan, and said, "Is this your passport?"

My father smiled. Yes, it was my passport. The cleaner saved us!

We passed through all the checks, ran to our gate, and boarded the plane.

I won't keep telling you everything we went through. Just one example: because we'd gotten tickets at the last minute, we didn't have time to order kosher meals, so we didn't have anything to eat, and we were starving. Luckily, we were so tired that we fell right asleep, and when you're sleeping, you don't eat—or get nauseous.

It was a twelve-hour flight. I woke up three hours before landing, and those three hours were the longest three hours in my life. I was hungry, and I really missed my mother. I was tired and worn out from all the difficulties we'd been through.

* * *

Finally, we landed. We passed through passport control, and then we collected our luggage and walked to the arrivals hall. Waiting there for us was Ima, who hugged and kissed us as if we'd been two weeks late.

She was crying, and we didn't understand why. So what if we were a day late? After all, we were the ones who'd suffered through it, not her.

When she calmed down, she told us something amazing.

"You have no idea of the drama that took place here," she said. "The news is filled with it!"

"What happened?" we asked.

"The pilot of the plane you were supposed to fly on noticed serious trouble with the wheel-locking mechanism halfway through the flight. If the wheels don't lock properly, the plane can crash on landing.

"Five hours before the plane was scheduled to land, the captain notified the passengers that there was a problem and that they should prepare for the worst. Everyone panicked. Some people screamed, some cried, some sat there frozen in place, and some said *tehillim*. Everyone was terrified. They'll never forget those five hours of terror as long as they live.

"Two hundred ambulances and dozens of fire engines sped to the airport here in case the plane was forced to land on its fuselage instead of its wheels. They assigned the plane a special runway that they covered with a thick layer of foam to prevent friction with the ground that could spark a fire.

"The plane also circled above the Tel Aviv harbor where it dumped fuel, which caused panic among the passengers. And then, as everyone held his breath, it landed. With *siyatta diShemaya*, the wheels locked into place, and the plane made a safe landing. The whole country—and especially the passengers—breathed a sigh of relief.

"You were spared all that," Ima said, "in the merit of guarding the sanctity of a *kohen*. You think you went through a stressful trip? Look what you were spared! A traumatic experience you'd never forget."

I thought to myself, *we kept the halachah that says a kohen can't be with a dead body and so we were saved from "deathly" fear.*

That's my story, and I think the point is that you *never* lose out by keeping halachah, even if you might think you're losing out. I chose to give this story a title that expresses the miracle we experienced because to sum it up in two words, we had a *"Birkas Kohanim."*

Lighting Up the World

My name is Meira.

I'm thirteen, and I live in Hadera.

My story is about a special boy. His life story is full of so much light that he could illuminate all the children and even Klal Yisrael. I'm talking about my big brother Yair.

When I say "my big brother," you probably imagine a physically big boy. My brother Yair is five years older than I am. He's eighteen, but he's not like a regular older brother.

Yair was born premature, and his development was delayed. He's always been slower, dreamier. He's never been like all the other kids, and now that he's a teen, he's not at all like the other boys his age.

When he was younger, he would sit in school like a potted plant, not bothering anyone and not learning anything either. But amazingly, his friends loved him, even though he didn't participate in their games. He was just too weak physically. They'd take care of him and try to include him in their own way. He'd run to bring them the ball, and they'd praise him. That's how they could include him in the game without ruining it for themselves. In return, they'd carry his backpack and let him be part of their group.

When they graduated, his friends went on to study in good yeshivahs, but Yair couldn't get into any school. So he stayed home.

If he was sad, he didn't show it. But we were sad enough for him. My mother explained to me that a regular educational institution wouldn't be a good match for him because of his developmental problems, and a place for people with delays wouldn't be good for him either because he wasn't in that category. We all knew he was pretty smart.

You might say that Yair fell between the cracks because he didn't fit into any specific category. But because of his personality, he was able to become a popular kid with tons of friends, and I'm not exaggerating. Anyone he met became his friend.

He'd do chores around the house, help my father with shopping and my mother with cooking. Between one thing and another, he'd talk to us, ask us questions, show an interest, and mostly, give compliments.

That's the point I want to emphasize. Yair would compliment a person on every single thing. For instance, he complimented our mother on her cooking (even though he helped her), me on my braid, someone else on their backpack. He'd express appreciation for the classes he attended, admire out loud the grades his friends got, and applaud the songs we sang. And he'd do it in such a special way. Whenever I finished singing a song, he'd say to me, "You sing so beautifully. Can you sing one more?"

He's so sweet, I feel like crying.

A few years ago I went shopping with Yair in the shuk. We filled up our shopping bags until they were loaded down with all sorts of stuff, but when we finished shopping, we realized we'd missed the last bus.

I knew we could never carry all the bags ourselves, because Yair, even though he is so much older than I, isn't strong at all. He is short and thin because he hasn't developed all that well, neither physically nor mentally, so all he could carry was two bags of light vegetables like parsley and green onion, and maybe a few apples. We didn't have a cellphone with us, and we were a few miles from our house.

"Do you have any money left for a taxi?" Yair asked me.

I hesitated because a taxi costs a lot more than a bus. But he convinced me that Abba wouldn't be upset and that if he was, Yair would pay for it from his pocket money.

I agreed.

A few minutes later, we flagged down a taxi. Like most taxi drivers, this one started talking and didn't stop. He explained everything we didn't know about everything that didn't interest us, like politics, wars, and all that kind of stuff. Naturally, I didn't pay any attention because I'm not interested in politics. But the driver was satisfied with an audience of one—my brother Yair. That audience turned out to be alert and interested. Fascinated, even.

When the taxi pulled up in front of our house, Yair said to the driver, "You know what? You're a really good driver."

"Very funny." The driver suspected Yair was making fun of him.

"I mean it," Yair said. "You're really a good driver. I see how you grip the steering wheel and how you squeezed your way through that narrow street where the blue car was parked too far from the curb. See? I'm not just saying it. You're not the usual driver, you're a pro."

The driver grinned like he'd just won the lottery.

"Listen, pint-size," he said. "I drive hundreds of people every day, but I've never gotten a single compliment about my driving."

"That's strange," Yair said. "You're such an exceptional driver, how could they miss it?"

"Maybe they take it for granted," the driver said. "The same way they don't tell a street sweeper what a great job he's doing. I mean, he's expected to sweep. That's his job."

"They probably don't understand driving," Yair consoled him. He didn't quite get what the driver meant about the street sweeper.

"Obviously," the driver said. "Good thing you do."

"Thank you," Yair said, his cheeks flushing. It didn't occur to him that the driver meant it cynically.

It was time to end this embarrassing conversation, so I asked the driver, "How much?"

The taxi driver thought for a moment and then said, "There's no need. I like your brother. The ride is gratis." (That means free.)

Yair liked that. "You gave us a free ride? You're a good man. You're the most professional taxi driver I've ever met and the kindest one, too."

"Thanks, kid. You're not so bad yourself," the driver said with real feeling.

We got out of the taxi with all our shopping bags and waved goodbye to the driver.

*   *   *

A week later, my older brother Nehorai told us an interesting story.

He was walking down the street with Yair when they passed a construction site where four workers were taking a lunch break. Yair stopped and stared at the building.

"Let's go," Nehorai said, but Yair ignored him and instead walked over to the workers.

"Hello, construction workers. Are you building this building?"

"Why do you ask?" they wanted to know.

"Because I think you've done an amazing job. I can't believe how you managed to build such a big, beautiful building."

By now, they were suspicious.

"Are you looking to get something from us?" one of them asked.

"Yes," Yair said. (He didn't really understand the question.) "I want you to tell me how you learned to

build. How do you manage to build without it falling? And how did you discover your talent at building?"

It took them a while to realize that he sincerely admired their work and wasn't making fun of them. They relaxed and opened up to him. They told him what they'd built, how they'd built, and the dangerous situations they'd faced. When they finished answering his questions, they parted from him as friends, and Yair said to them, "It's people like you who build the world."

Nehorai told us that the workers looked like they'd just won a prize. Which reminded me of the taxi driver.

On the way home, Nehorai said to Yair, "You know something? I think the building contractor should pay you."

"For what?" Yair asked, puzzled.

"I'm sure those workers are going to work extra hard and do some really outstanding work now, at least in the next few days.

*   *   *

We got used to the fact that Yair makes people feel good. He takes an interest in them, asks them questions, and gives them compliments. Lots. But they aren't just random words of approval. They're to the point and very convincing. Yair is like his name: he brings light to other people. And most of all, he gives us all a good feeling, every single one of us, and we weren't even aware of it at first.

It took us time to realize that he is like a fire, warming everyone around him with his light. Maybe he isn't the most developed kid around, but he brings light to everyone around him, and everyone returns his love.

* * *

Before my bas mitzvah, my parents and I sat down to plan the program.

Girls do all sorts of things. Some do a family history project. Some take on a *chesed* project. And some just want a super fancy party with dancing and activities.

But I had a different idea.

"I think I want to do something my friends haven't seen before. Not the usual stuff. Something that will make them better and want to improve themselves."

My parents raised their eyebrows in a mixture of astonishment and skepticism.

"Do you want us to bring a speaker to talk about improving one's *middos*?" my father asked. I know him well enough to know from the way he said it that he didn't think my friends would go for that.

"Meira," my mother said, "improving our *middos*

is so important, but at a bas mitzvah party girls also expect to have a little fun. Maybe we can think of some kind of special play that would include all those values."

"I already thought of something," I said.

I presented my idea to them. They were so surprised, they didn't know what to say at first. Then they wondered if my idea was even possible and if it was, how it would go over. In the end, I managed to convince them that it was what I really wanted to do and that it could be spectacular if we did it the right way.

Over the next two months, our whole family worked with professionals on this special project. We kept it a family secret. No one else knew about. It was all hush-hush. A week before my bas mitzvah, we knew we had something special, something that had never been done before.

*   *   *

The party started out like most parties, with decorations, a special sweet table, and lots of great food.

We danced and then laughed out loud at a comedian's skits. Toward the end, we asked everyone (and "everyone" included close family and distant relatives plus my friends) to take seats in front of a giant screen.

None of the guests knew what to expect. Actually, they all expected the usual: clips of me growing up, set to music, and a poem written in honor of my bas mitzvah that one of my friends would read aloud. You know, something like, "Meira, you're the best / you pass every test / happy bas mitzvah from us to you / and lots of success in all you do."

But instead, big, bold letters appeared on the screen:

"LIGHTING UP THE WORLD."
MEIRA'S BAS MITZVAH PROJECT.

It was a movie about Yair.

For two months we'd filmed him as he went through his day showing an interest in everyone he met, asking them questions, and mostly being amazed by them and giving them compliments. It was funny, it was fascinating, it was entertaining, it was unbelievable. And mostly, it was moving to the point of tears.

As the director, I approached the theme from several angles. One was "Yair with people." But I wove into the video interviews with those same people—with the grocer, with the barber, and even with the taxi driver (it took us time to locate him), and with dozens of people Yair shone his light on. They all said how Yair, with his simple words, made their day. They said he showed them respect, made them feel good, and even found positive aspects of themselves they'd been unaware of.

They had a lot of good things to say about Yair. They said he was all heart. What I discovered is that people are happy when someone sings their praises in public. When I think about it, it's so obvious. We all like people to say good things about us in front of friends, teachers, and even our parents, who know us. But I learned from the film that it's important even for parents to have people tell them nice things about their children.

Which is exactly what Yair did, and you could see it in the video. He didn't miss a thing. He got everyone to feel good about themselves and got others to view him with respect. Everyone could see the light that this boy, my brother, was spreading.

At the end of the film, I appeared on the screen and spoke directly to my friends and family. This is what I said:

"I decided to make this video about my beloved brother Yair for my bas mitzvah. His name says it all: Yair, whose light shines on other people. Some people might think that life didn't exactly light up his world. But because of his own inner light that he shines on others, life does shine its special light on him.

"I thought a lot about this special ability of his. Why

doesn't everyone have it? Are we all blind? Don't we realize that giving is called receiving? That giving a compliment changes the world—especially your own world?

"We all just saw what a kind word can do, how it changes the world for good, and also your own world.

"Today, the day of my bas mitzvah, I'm asking everyone to please leave here with a big flashlight to light up the world."

The film ended.

* * *

Ever since, till this very day, no one has forgotten my bas mitzvah.

My class changed. Every girl tries to light up the world, to do *chesed*.

I hope every boy and girl who reads this story will take the idea and decide to light up the world. All you need are kind words, a smiling face, compliments, and kindness.

Try it, and our world will be a lot better place. And when it happens, no one will forget where this change started and who gets the credit.

Yair, my fabulous brother.

Neighbors Like That

My name is Lele.

I'm twelve, and I live in a big city.

You're probably wondering why I'm not telling you which city. Don't worry, you'll find out soon enough.

My story began eight years ago.

We used to live in a nice building with nice neighbors, and everything was great with them. As our family grew, things got crowded. Us kids wanted the family to move to a bigger place, and we pretty much let our parents know how we felt. My father told us, "You're right. It *is* crowded here, but we have such nice neighbors it'd be a shame to move."

What he said didn't make much of an impression on us, and we campaigned for a move. We told our parents it was impossible to live like that anymore and said we couldn't do homework and that we had no

room to move and there was no closet space and....
You get the picture.

In the end, our parents gave in, and one day, my father announced that the time had come for us to move,
and so it was.

We moved to a different apartment in a different
neighborhood. That's when we realized that we hadn't
taken one point into consideration (even though our
parents had talked about it), and that was saying goodbye to our neighbors.

It wasn't easy to leave them. It meant saying goodbye to the childhood friends we'd known since we were
born, to the neighborhood games, to the back-and-forth
in each other's homes. It was really heartbreaking.

We didn't dare say anything to our parents because
we were the ones who had driven them crazy about
the move. But they understood how we felt without
us saying anything. They consoled us by saying we'd
continue to be friends with everyone in our old neighborhood and that the distance wouldn't separate us.
Stuff like that. We appreciated their caring about us,
but we were pretty sure things wouldn't work out that
way.

But that wasn't the worst.

Besides missing our old neighborhood, we had

another problem. My parents weren't able to find a buyer for the old apartment. My father was under a lot of financial pressure, so he took out a loan to pay for the new apartment until he could sell the old one. (I remember that they called it a "balloon loan," which I thought was really funny.)

We were sure we'd make new friends and have nice new neighbors. Instead, it was a catastrophe.

*   *   *

The trouble started about half a year after we moved. Or, to put it more clearly, the downstairs neighbors were our trouble.

During the first six months, we were friendly. We played games outside together and traded stickers. Stuff like that.

But one Shabbos my sister jumped rope inside the house, something she was used to doing all the time. All of a sudden, the downstairs neighbors' daughter came upstairs and said it was bothering them.

Okay. We could understand that. Maybe the mother didn't feel well. My sister stopped jumping rope.

Then one day, in the middle of the day, my brother was playing *kugelach,* and they came up again, saying it was bothering them. And that's how it went every day and every hour of the day. Every time we moved a chair, they'd come upstairs.

Because we were on the top floor, my mother said we should go play on the roof. Turns out that bothered them even more. They came up and started shouting that the noise reached their window two floors below.

Last year in Adar, my brother was on his riding toy. He was barely on it for two minutes when the neighbor came upstairs and started shouting. I won't repeat what she said. It was too awful. And for what? A riding toy?

Shouting wasn't enough for her. It was winter, and we put our umbrellas outside the front door. There were about three umbrellas there. She took them and began ramming them into our door, which made a deep scratch in our front door, broke all the umbrellas, and knocked down the mezuzah. We had a picture hanging on the hall wall right outside the entrance to our apartment. She took it off the wall and destroyed the pretty wood frame. She rang the doorbell over and over again.

All this was accompanied by screams.

We were standing behind the door (which, luckily for us was closed, because if it hadn't been, she might have continued her rampage inside the house, too). We didn't know what to do. My little brother started to cry, and my mother didn't know how to calm him down. She called my father.

"What should we do?"

My father said that it was a good opportunity to work on our *middos.* "Let's see how we can meet this challenge."

So my mother and my older sisters and I and my older brothers sat around the table and began singing, *"Kol haolam hazeh gesher tzar meod, gesher tzar meod."* We sang and cried at the same time. Those were special moments when we all felt ourselves going higher spiritually.

We realized that it wasn't just a matter of neighbors disagreeing. They actually—

I don't even want to say it. I'm sure you know what I mean.

* * *

One day, my four-year-old brother went to visit his friend who lived across the street.

On the way, he met the neighbors' youngest child, a boy of twelve. He was holding a toy gun that looked real.

He came up to my brother and said, "I'm going to kill you!"

Think of what goes through a four-year-old's mind:

That's it! I'm going to die. He's bigger than me, and he has a real gun!

My brother started to run home, and the neighbor boy aimed the gun at him and shot. I don't think my brother noticed it was only water coming out. He raced for home like a wild animal. He flung open the door and bawled his head off, screaming like someone who had just escaped sudden death. His face was white.

My mother couldn't figure out what had happened to him. He was crying too hard to talk at first, but little by little, he started telling us, in his childish language, that they almost killed him.

My mother told us we should encourage him to talk about it because it would help him get over the trauma. We calmed him down, and the next day, my father took him to a toy store to show him that it wasn't a real gun and couldn't kill anyone. Then he really calmed down.

* * *

The straw that broke the camel's back was Simchas Torah.

We invited our former neighbors to join us for Yom Tov (remember, here in Eretz Yisrael Shemini Atzeres and Simchas Torah are the same day). They had little kids, and they played upstairs with my younger brothers and sisters. It was about eleven in the morning, before the *seudah*. All of a sudden, our front door flew open, and there stood the downstairs neighbor, his face a fiery red.

Everyone knows that a person's home is his castle, his private domain where he's safe and secure, but he'd just violated that rule. He burst into our home as if he owned it.

"Who was jumping in here?!" he screamed. Meanwhile, his wife was letting out bloodcurdling screams from their apartment below.

My married sister, who was also with us for the holiday, was terrified.

"What do you want?" she asked him fearfully.

He went closer as if to hit her—and she's so tiny, and he's so big and fat. It was scary.

My sister's husband, my brother-in-law, was afraid for his wife's safety, so he blocked the man from getting any closer. The neighbor was infuriated and with one slap, sent my brother-in-law spinning across the room so hard that his glasses flew off.

My father was scared, but he went to help his son-in-law. The neighbor knocked my father down, too.

Not only is my father not all that young, but he's a distinguished Rav and looks like one. And that's what

this neighbor did to him! It hurts me to remember the scene and to write about seeing my father and brother-in-law on the floor, everyone standing around terrified and crying. And then the neighbor said something so horrifying that we'll never forget it. He said, "This is the end of you all!" and stormed out.

As soon as he left, we all cried, adults and children alike—and on Simchas Torah no less, the happiest day of the year.

My father was a real hero. He consoled us by saying that it was a test and that Hashem loves us because He brings suffering only to those He loves.

The holiday was sad straight through till the end. We keep Rabbeinu Tam time, which, as you probably know, means we make Havdalah at least half an hour after Shabbos or Yom Tov finishes. Well, the second Yom Tov was over, we heard loud knocks on the front door.

The police!

* * *

The neighbors probably thought we would call the police (they'd never dream that my father is a *vatran*, and is the last person to fight. And why should they? They don't know what it means to give in.) So they decided to accuse my father of doing the hitting, instead of the other way round.

The policemen told my father that they'd come to arrest him.

My father told them that they should first find out what actually happened, but they said that's not their job. They were there to arrest him and his son-in-law, and police inspectors would investigate the charges.

My father asked if he could make Havdalah before they took them, and the policemen said okay.

I'll never forget that Havdalah. My father made the *berachos* in his usual pleasant, sweet voice as if he didn't have a care in the world! All the children gathered around the table, scared and worried. The minute Havdalah ended, the policemen told my father and brother-in-law that they were forbidden to take anything with them—not even a cell phone or a wallet! Nothing!!! They'd be cut off from everyone. We wouldn't have any way to keep in contact with them. And then...*this is so hard for me to write*...they put handcuffs on them!

Until this day our parents are sorry that they didn't send us to another room so that we wouldn't have to see such a horrible thing. It was so shocking; it really shook us up.

It was also very humiliating because everyone on our street—and I mean *everyone*—was looking out the window. (Ever since, whenever I see someone being loaded onto an ambulance, I go the other way so as not to embarrass them.)

After they left, we all gathered in the living room and cried tears of frustration, shame, fear, and worry. All our worries were in those tears, and my mother had no idea how to console us. That's how the night went until midnight.

That's when my father came home.

We were so happy!

This is what he told us: "They made us wait a long time. Then they put us in a room and told us that we were charged with a crime of violence."

My father went on to say that, as he had suspected, the neighbor had come up with this plan over the holiday. He was afraid we'd call the police on him, so he injured himself and then, as soon as the holiday was over, called the police and charged his neighbor (my father) and the neighbor's son-in-law with causing the injury.

My father told the police investigators the true story. He also proved it with photographic evidence that showed the damages the neighbor had done to our place. He suggested that they check with other neighbors to find out who hit whom. They did just that and became convinced that the neighbor was the one who had done the hitting and had made up the story.

The officers apologized and released them.

*   *   *

All this time, our former neighbors stayed with us to give us support. When my father and brother-in-law returned, our former neighbors said, "It's not by chance that this happened exactly when we're here. It's all from Above. We think you need to move back to our building. Everyone misses you. It would be great if you came back. You didn't sell the place yet, so sell this apartment and come back to us and everything will go back to being peaceful."

"But we need more room. The old place is crowded."

"We wouldn't mind living in even one room as long as we move away from here," we kids piped up.

"I have good news for you," our old neighbor said. "We've decided to add on to the building. Everyone's for it, and they've all signed. You'll have another two rooms and a big porch."

"What?!" my father exclaimed.

"Yay!" we all cried.

* * *

We stayed where we were for another year. The neighbors no longer dared do anything to us because the police arrested the violent neighbor and kept him in jail for a few days before bringing him to trial. He was nervous about his court case and didn't want to make things worse for himself, but the atmosphere was terrible.

Eventually, my father was able to sell the apartment, and for a better price than he'd paid for it. With the extra money, he was able to pay for the expansion of our original apartment. Once the renovations were finished, we went back to live in the building we'd loved and to our wonderful neighbors who were as happy as we were about our return.

* * *

So here we are, settled in our home, and anyone who doesn't know the story has no idea what a difference it made in our lives.

My father likes to say about it, "From the bitter came the sweet." The whole adventure (if you can call it that) was probably to let us pay for the expansion.

But more than that, my father says, now we understand what a gift Hashem gave us all those years, one we didn't appreciate at the time. We had to move somewhere else to realize how grateful we needed to be to Hashem for giving us such good neighbors. It's not something you can take for granted, he told us. And because we passed the test, we saw a lot of good that came out of it.

My father suggested to us that we always thank Hashem for our health, our success in school, and all the many things we have. That way, Hashem won't have to give us a test to teach us the lesson of gratitude in a hard way. I know that I started to really appreciate all the good things Hashem gives me in my life after this happened.

I also want to say that even when the going is tough, we need to remember that Hashem loves us, and we should take advantage of those special moments to daven to Him in the merit of "those who are insulted but don't take it to heart." Also, we need to remember that in those moments of panic and stress, the first thing to do is to take the children away so that what they witness won't scar them for life. It's hard, because, during those few minutes of panic, you can forget, and then you'll regret it.

But even if we did experience fear, we can move past it if we realize that from bad can come good.

*   *   *

The end of this story is the neighbor's trial.

He sent people to my father, asking him to forgive him and to speak well of him in court.

What do you think my father did?

You're right.

The judge was very moved by this. He said that according to testimony, the neighbor committed a violent act against my father and his son-in-law, and then added to his crime by falsely accusing my father of attacking him. If the truth hadn't come out, this could have ruined my father's life. The judge couldn't understand how my father could ask the court to have mercy on the neighbor and said that my father is a real tzaddik (which he is).

The judge said that he was ready to sentence the accused to serve time in jail, but due to my father's pleas he was going to suspend the charges of violence and only sentence him to compensate our family.

After the trial was over, the neighbor cried and pleaded with my father to forgive him. He said he was sorry we were moving because we were good neighbors and the problem was with him.

That's the end of the story. That's what we went through, and I think it's a story that will probably interest a lot of kids, even the ones who never had any problems with their neighbors. At least they'll know to thank Hashem for what they have.

In a Place Where There Are No Men

My name is Meir.

I'm eleven, and I live in the center of the country.

I want to tell you a story about my friend Danny. His story got a lot of publicity, but I think it belongs in *Kids Speak* because kids don't necessarily read adult newspapers, and I think it's very important for kids to read this story.

I know that Danny won't be the one to tell you the story because he's not the type to brag. But there's so much to learn from what happened that I want to tell it. Naturally, without revealing Danny's last name.

Danny is one of the best kids in our class. He's not a big talker, but he's not the silent type, either. He just doesn't say what doesn't need to be said. When something does need to be said, he talks—and everyone listens.

Danny is a good boy and a mature boy. He always stands up for the weaker kids, and he always notices when a kid is having a hard time with something or is feeling down. Then he'll show an interest and try to help.

Danny once told me that his father taught him to follow what it says in *Pirkei Avos* 2:5: "In a place where there are no men, strive to be a man." He explained to me that there are all kinds of things kids run into and think it's none of their business. Usually, it's true, because it's up to adults to take care of adult matters.

"But if you see something wrong or someone who needs help, and no one notices, or they do notice but don't do anything," he told me, "then you be the one to go and do something, like call an adult or an emergency number like 101 in Israel or 911 in the States or the fire department or police, and make sure that the right person comes to help."

And really, whenever you need Danny, he's right there. If we're on a class trip and someone needs something, Danny's the one who will give it to him. If a kid gets stuck in school without food, Danny will go down to the secretary's office and make sure they give the student money to buy food. In other words, you can count on him.

When the incident that made headlines took place, everyone except us was in shock. We weren't surprised at all, because we already knew him.

*   *   *

It happened during summer vacation. Danny went with his family on vacation to Meron, and one day he went with his father on a day trip further north.

They took bicycles and headed for Tzefas. From there, they planned to reach the Ein Koves spring. Along the way, Danny's father told him that this spring had other names as well. It's called "The well of Binyamin Hatzaddik" and "Ein Pinchas." The name Ein Koves comes because people used to wash clothes in its water (the Hebrew word for washing clothes is *koves*). He also said that people come there to *tovel* in it on Fridays.

Once, when they took a short break, Danny's father told him a story about Binyamin Hatzaddik from the Gemara in *Bava Basra*: Binyamin Hatzaddik ran a charity fund. Once, a woman came to him during a drought and pleaded with him, "Rabbi, sustain me!" Rabbi Binyamin told her that there was no money in the charity fund.

But the woman didn't give up. "Rabbi, if you don't sustain me, then I and my seven sons will die."

Rabbi Binyamin gave her money from the little he had and saved her and her family.

Several years passed, and Rabbi Binyamin fell deathly ill. The angels said to Hashem, "*Ribbono shel Olam*, You said that when a person sustains the life of a Jew, it's as if he sustained the whole world. Why should Binyamin Hatzaddik, who sustained a woman and her seven sons, die at such a young age?"

Right then and there, his sentence was torn up in Heaven, and twenty-two years were added to his life.

* * *

The story made a big impression on Danny, and both of them, father and son, continued to pedal their way to the fascinating spring.

After two hours of biking, ten minutes from the stream, Danny's father suddenly stopped and said to Danny, "Let's rest. I don't feel so good."

They stopped and sat down on a large rock.

Then Danny's father said to him, "It's strange. I really don't feel good," and all of a sudden, he passed out on the ground.

Danny was terrified. He tried to wake his father by shouting, "Abba! Abba! Wake up!" But his father made no response.

For a moment, Danny panicked. He looked around to see if anyone was nearby. When he realized they were alone, he said to himself, *I have to figure out what Abba would tell me to do.* In a flash, his father's favorite quote came to mind: "In a place where there are no men, strive to be a man."

Danny took his father's cell phone out of his father's shirt pocket. But the phone was code protected.

Only a few months earlier, his father had explained to him that every mobile device has an emergency call button so that Magen David Adom or the police or fire department can be called even if you don't know the phone's code.

Danny quickly found the emergency call button, pressed it, and then dialed 100, which in Israel is the number for the police.

"Shalom," he said when a voice answered the call. "This is Danny speaking. We're on a trip, and my father fainted, and he's not answering me."

"Remain on the line," the responder said. "I'm transferring you to Magen David Adom."

Magen David Adom is Israel's national emergency medical response organization.

At Magen David Adom, a medic by the name of Yana took the call.

"My name is Danny," Danny told Yana. "My father is lying here collapsed, I guess because he's exhausted."

"Let me talk to an adult who's there with you," Yana said.

"There is no adult here with me. It's just the two of us, and we're in the middle of the mountain."

"Try calling him," Yana told him.

Danny shouted, "Abba! Abba!" but his father didn't respond.

"He's not waking up," Danny said.

"Where are you?" Yana asked.

"I'm at Ein Koves near Tzefas," Danny said. "We're alone. In the middle of the mountain."

The medic quickly realized that only Danny could save his father.

"How old are you, Danny?"

"I'm eleven."

Yana was very worried that an eleven-year-old wouldn't be able to help. You can understand why. But she didn't know Danny.

"Look, Danny," Yana said, "because there is no adult there, we'll try to do whatever is necessary to save your father."

Yana needed an accurate picture of the father's health in general to figure out what led to his collapse so that she could guide Danny through the steps to stabilize his father's condition.

"Is your father breathing? Does he have any illnesses? Did he drink enough?"

Danny answered her questions, calmly and maturely. "He's breathing. I checked that. But he's unconscious. He doesn't respond to me. I don't think he has any illnesses. I think he's just exhausted. We were riding our bikes for a while and we've been walking on the trail for two hours already, and he drank a lot. Then, all of a sudden, he told me he couldn't go on anymore."

Yana asked Danny to look for a sweet food in his father's backpack. Danny found some chocolate, and Yana instructed him to smear it on his father's gums (because sometimes people lose consciousness because their blood-sugar level drops).

Danny reported to Yana that his father's lip color was light pink. He also checked his father's body heat and told Yana that it was very warm.

Yana told him to take a bottle of cold water and place it on his father's body. Danny told her they had a towel and asked if she thought it better to wet the towel and put it on his father's forehead. Yana told him it was really a better idea, so Danny did it.

Throughout this time, Danny acted bravely and resolutely, continually calling his father and not giving up even though he didn't answer.

*   *   *

Yana asked Danny to try to find people around him, but there was no one nearby. He smeared more chocolate on his father's gums, then told Yana, "My father opened his eyes a little, but he can't talk."

Yana tried to figure out where they were. Danny didn't know, but he estimated they were about half a mile from the road. He continued to give Yana information about their location. Thanks to this information, MDA teams were eventually able to locate him and his father, aided by police tracking the signal of his father's cell phone.

"Great job," the medic at MDA's 101 hotline kept praising Danny all the time.

As MDA teams approached the area, Yana told Danny, "I need you to shout as loud as you can. As soon as you hear the helicopter, ambulance, or police forces we sent, tell me immediately."

About half an hour from the start of the call, MDA's first team arrived. The team commander took the phone from Danny and said, "This is Shimon Bismuth, MDA

paramedic. We reached them. Everything's okay."

"Great!" Yana said and praised Danny, the hero, who kept calm and saved his father's life.

Danny's father received life-saving medical treatment from the MDA medics and paramedics. While sedated and on a ventilator, he was evacuated with Danny by military helicopter for further treatment at Ziv Hospital in Tzefas. A few days later, he was released from the hospital in good condition.

*   *   *

This story, including the recording of the conversation between Yana and Danny, was publicized on radio and in newspapers. The medic, Yana Hush, said, "Thousands of calls are received every day at the 101 hotline of Magen David Adom, and every paramedic who operates the hotline, like me, helps about 150 civilians in various medical emergencies, every day. But I never thought I'd encounter an eleven-year-old on the line with such maturity and determination, saving his father, all alone and so bravely while remaining calm."

Even Magen David Adom's director-general Eli Bin was very impressed. "The eleven-year-old is a real hero. His performance during this emergency played a major role in saving his father's life," he said.

The whole country was excited by the story, and when I heard what happened there, I actually cried. But I can't say I was surprised. Everyone who knows Danny knows it was just like him to act that way—mature, practical, and determined to help as best he could.

For sure, I don't wish it on any kid to have to deal with a situation like this. But if he does find himself in a situation where a family member, a friend, or even a stranger on the street is in distress, he'll be happy he read about what Danny did. Because he'll know what to do and how to act: call for help, follow instructions, and stay cool, calm, and collected.

Truth Always Triumphs

My name is Michal, but most people call me Michali.

I'm learning in a religious school now but until ninth grade, I learned in public school. Don't get me wrong. I always believed in Hashem. It's just that I didn't know how to express that love. (By doing mitzvos, of course.)

I want to share with you the stories that made me who I am today. They proved to me the power of the truth and the importance of kindness.

The story about truth happened when I was in fifth grade. I was part of a group of three. We weren't especially popular, but that didn't matter to us because we spent all our time together.

I'd advise every girl to act the way I did — to make a few good friends and not to envy the popular girls, or worse, flatter them and try to push your way into their circle. It doesn't work, and it ruins your self-confidence.

What happened to us was that a group of "in" girls that wasn't so big—maybe it had five or six girls, tops—weren't content to be queens of the class *and* the whole world but wanted to put us down in front of the whole class.

Things got worse, but none of us three had the courage to answer them back or tell the teacher.

We knew that if we told the teacher, the girls would deny it, and not a single girl in the class would say they were lying. We'd wind up looking not only like tattletales but liars. So, we just accepted their bullying in silence.

* * *

One day, during gym class, the teacher divided our class into three groups. Two groups competed against each other in a basketball game while the third group watched. Then the third group played the winner.

To our good fortune, my two friends and I were put in the same group, and the "in" crowd was placed in another. We were thrilled because we knew that if we were together with them, they wouldn't be our teammates but our enemies. They'd do everything they could to make us fail. They wouldn't pass us the ball even if it meant the team lost the game.

The first game started with us playing against the third group, the one those girls weren't in. It was a fast-paced game, and we all had a lot of fun. Then we played against the group with the "in" girls. They played *very* aggressively. They pushed us when the teacher wasn't looking, and every basket we sank through the net drew boos and snide remarks from them about what terrible players we really were and how it was just luck, etc.

When the game was over, we went to sit down on the pile of gym mats where the group that wasn't playing sat and watched. The group we had played against first, got up to play against the "in" group's team, and we sat down to watch.

My friends and I didn't talk to each other about what had happened, but it was obvious the three of us were about to explode with rage. How much longer could we take their bullying?

We didn't know what to do.

We sat there watching the game. I don't know about my two friends, but I prayed for them to lose. No one could see I was praying. It wasn't a prayer that came from the right place. It was coming from the huge ball of anger inside me.

I raised my eyes and said to my Father in Heaven,

"Abba! Please! They don't deserve to win! Make them lose. Just so they'll be a little less snobby, just to prove to them that they're not better than everyone else. Please, Abba! Make them lose."

That very second, the group playing against them made the first basket of the game. I was so excited, I cried out, "*Yes!*" My two friends, who I knew wanted the bullying girls to lose, joined me in applauding and cheering the group that made the basket. We saw it irritated the bullying girls, but we couldn't stop.

Every time the neutral group made a basket, we cheered and clapped. And every time the "in" girls' group made a basket, we booed. I knew it wasn't nice. But everything I'd kept inside for such a long time, all the anger I felt toward them, just came out like that. It became more and more focused and hurtful, until, after a few baskets, those girls were boiling mad.

They came over to us and started shouting and putting us down. We couldn't have cared less. It felt so good to release our pent-up anger and resentment and give them a taste of everything they'd done to us. The teacher quickly separated us and decided to stop the competition and to let our class out early.

* * *

Just before we went back to our classroom, the most dominant girl in the "in" group, the one who usually bullied us while the others added their support, hissed at us, "You think you're going to get away with this? Just you wait and see what trouble you're going to be in." She went up to the classroom with the rest of the "in" group trailing after her.

We looked at each other. We knew just what she had in mind. We knew that the next day there'd be investigations and for the first time, we'd be to blame. I didn't want to think about the punishment we'd get.

"It won't be that bad," one of my friends said. "They won't give us anything worse than cleaning the school or the yard."

"Maybe," the second one said. "*If* they tell the truth. And that's a big if. There are six of them, and only three of us. The teacher will believe them even if they lie."

She was right. It was clear to the three of us that they were going to blow up this unpleasant incident for all it was worth by embellishing it with all sorts of things that never happened.

We went home. I didn't have the strength or patience for anyone in my family. I went straight to my room and stayed there. I knew everyone must be worried, but I was ashamed of myself. How could I have acted that way? I'd acted in the same lowly manner as the "in" group.

I didn't care about the inquiry or even about the punishment I'd get. I felt bad, like it was my fault. Yes, those girls had acted badly to me. But to become just like them in order to repay them? I was very mad at myself.

Time dragged. Regret and self-blame churned within me.

That night, my little brother lay in the trundle bed of our bunk bed, and I was in the top bunk staring at the ceiling. I peeked down and saw he'd fallen asleep. My baby sister in the next room was also asleep. Eventually, my parents fell asleep too. I tossed and turned.

It was late. I prayed to Hashem the whole night (remember, I still wasn't religious yet, but I talked to Him a lot every day). I felt so ashamed of myself. I felt that Hashem was definitely disappointed in me. I pulled the covers up over my head and burst out crying.

I couldn't stand the thought that Hashem was angry with me. Would He ever forgive me?

"Abba in Heaven!" I whispered under my covers. "I'm sorry! I'm so, so sorry! I know You're probably angry with me, but I'm asking You to forgive me even if I don't deserve it. I should have stopped myself. I shouldn't have asked for them to lose. I gave in to my anger toward them. I didn't stop to think that it's wrong to act that way."

I cried for about half an hour, and then I promised myself that during the investigation the next day I wouldn't even try to defend myself. I'd admit the truth about everything I'd done, and I'd graciously accept the punishment I had coming to me. Though I knew that my two friends wouldn't do the same, I would— even if I was the only one punished. I deserved to be punished alone!

"I'm sorry, Hashem," I whispered, and closed my eyes.

I felt better after that prayer. I felt that Hashem heard me and that He would forgive me if I'd make sure to fix things. And that made me feel good.

* * *

The next day, I nearly jumped out of bed. I got ready for school quickly, surprising my parents, because usually, I was late. On the ride to school I didn't talk even though I felt much better. My father tried to engage me in conversation, but finally gave up and talked with my brother instead. I kissed my father on

the cheek, got out of the car, and walked through the school gate.

The teacher responsible for investigating the incident saw me making my way to the classroom and told me that the investigation would take place during the second period. She asked me to arrive on time at the room where the investigation would be held.

The first period dragged. I looked at my friends. They seemed tense, and fidgeted with items on their desks.

I turned to look back at the "in" group. The class queen smiled victoriously at me as if to say, "Let's see how you're going to get out of this one!"

I quickly turned my head around and thought, *Give me the strength to fix this!* Now I knew it was going to be a lot worse than I'd thought. Still, I'd made up my mind to go through with my plan no matter what.

After the first class ended, a teacher entered the classroom and said, "The girls of the investigation— Morah Leah is calling you."

The "in" group stood up quickly and walked out of the classroom looking very proud. I gathered my things slowly, trying to postpone the inevitable. Up until now, I couldn't wait for the investigation, but now that the time had arrived, I wanted to push it off.

* * *

I felt all eyes on me as I walked out of the classroom after my two friends. Not a single classmate wanted to have anything to do with us. I went into the restroom and then walked to the room where the investigation would take place. By the time I arrived, everyone else was already there. The class queen gave me a smile that cut through me like a knife, and the teacher asked me why I was late.

I apologized for being late and sat down at the side, next to one of my friends. I pushed my chair back a little and wished I could fade into the wall. Somehow become invisible.

The teacher began to speak. She repeated what she had heard about what happened and then asked each girl to describe the incident from her point of view. She invited the class queen to speak first, followed by the girls in her group.

Most of the girls in the "in" group repeated whatever the "queen" said without changing a thing. Naturally, they didn't mention their constant mockery and put-downs of us. They also didn't say that they'd made fun of us during the game.

I wondered how they could remember so many lies. Maybe they'd coordinated their stories before the investigation.

Actually, already at night, when I'd thought of it, I knew the hardest part would be forcing myself to tell the truth. But now I felt it would be even more difficult than I'd imagined, because to listen to all these awful lies and not say anything would be unbearable.

At that moment, I felt as if Hashem put His hand over my mouth and whispered to me, "It's better for you not to answer. You want to repair the damage and not destroy anymore, don't you?"

My friends tried to tell the teacher that it was all lies, but she hushed them and told them that they'd have a turn to tell their version.

Finally, they spoke as well, and the more they talked, the more I realized how much trouble I was in. They lied, contradicting both the lies of the other girls and the truth of what actually happened. I saw the class queen turn red. She shouted something at them and was told by the teacher to wait, just like my friends had been told to wait their turn.

What was said in that room was a mixture of lies and exaggerations. Not a single girl accepted responsibility, and each one exaggerated what the other group had done.

*   *   *

When my friends finished talking, the teacher turned to me and asked me to give my version of what happened. I pushed my chair back a little further. It hit the wall. I looked down. I saw my knees shaking from fear and embarrassment, and I started to talk.

I couldn't bring myself to look at the teacher, but I could easily imagine her stern look and the triumphant looks of the "in" group girls, and worst of all, the totally shocked look of my friends. I knew I was harming only myself and that nothing would happen to them. Out of the corner of my eye, I could see their expressions. I lowered my eyes further until I could no longer see anyone in the room.

This is what I said:

"Mrs. Brown, I admit to everything they blamed me for. It's true. I did everything I could to annoy them. I gloated over their misses. I prayed for them to lose. Every word that came out of my mouth and every clap I made was to bother them. But I'm sorry it came out that way. I know I wasn't right, and I know I deserve a punishment. They're not to blame for the quarrel. It wouldn't have happened if I hadn't pushed them to do what they did. My friends aren't to blame either. They just followed me."

Everyone in the room was shocked, including the teacher. They hadn't thought I'd say anything like that. My friends didn't know what had come over me, and the "in" girls, who'd looked smug when I first began speaking, had the smiles wiped off their faces.

The teacher seemed surprised. She'd been expecting to hear a different version. And then, instead of speaking to me in a strict tone of voice as she'd done with the others, she asked me softly, "Michal, can you tell me why you acted like that? Why were you happy to see them fail? Why did you pray for them to lose? That's not the Michal I know."

I thought a little, and then I lifted my head and looked into her eyes.

"There's a reason, but that doesn't make it right. But there is a reason. I think they know exactly what made good girls like us want them to lose and to be happy at their defeat. I can't say what that reason is, but they know it, and if they want to, they can say what it was." And then I burst out crying and sobbed, "It doesn't make what I did right. It's not nice to pay them back and in front of the whole class, no less. I'm sorry!"

I wiped the tears from my cheeks and lowered my

eyes, ready to accept whatever was coming to me. I knew I'd done the right thing by telling the truth even if it was painful.

The room was quiet. I glanced at my friends' faces. They looked shocked. I lowered my gaze again.

And then I heard the teacher say, "Girls, I heard several versions of the events that took place yesterday, but the only one who spoke the truth was Michal." I looked up in panic, not understanding what she meant. She smiled at me and said, "Michal, you may return to class. I learned a lesson from you today."

*   *   *

My heart was pounding, and I felt shaky as I left the room and closed the door behind me. I went into my classroom, still in shock and unable to talk. The girls in my class were surprised to see me walk in alone and bombarded me with questions.

I didn't answer. I just sat down in my seat.

Thank You, thank You, thank You, thank You! I said in my heart.

Then the other girls returned to the classroom. The whole class could see that something momentous had taken place. During recess, girls came over to me one by one and said, "Michali, you're special. We didn't

appreciate you enough before. You're something else."
I couldn't believe I was hearing such things.

Then I found out the teacher had suggested they compare themselves with me and try to understand why she'd let me off without any punishment. She then asked the other girls to continue where I'd left off and tell her what made me and my friends eager to witness their humiliation.

It worked. Like me, they started admitting the truth, telling about their repeated insults, their mockery, their patronizing attitude, and their exclusion of us from the group. There were a lot of tears but there was also a lot of willingness to change, and the main thing is, a lot of truth.

All because of the plain and simple truth I'd contributed to the meeting when it was my turn to speak.

* * *

Things worked out after that, you could say. I'm not saying I became part of the "in" group. But the bullying stopped and was replaced by a good relationship between me and all the girls in my class. I took that as a sign Hashem forgave me. Mostly it reinforced in me the determination to always tell the truth, because not only did I not get punished for what I did, but I was even rewarded.

At the beginning of this story, I said that what made me become religious was the power of truth and the importance of kindness. You just heard the story about truth. I didn't tell the story about kindness yet, but I will when the time is right. *B'ezras Hashem.*

The Great Escape

My name is Yoni.

I'm eleven, and I live in Yerushalayim.

Until last year, I lived in Tzefas. We moved to Yerushalayim at the beginning of the school year.

I want to tell you about the move from city to city and mostly about the move to a new school and new friends.

When we first heard that we'd be moving to a new city, we felt bad. Not a single one of my brothers and sisters wanted to leave the place we'd grown up in, and we sure didn't want to leave our school. But most of all, we didn't want to leave the friends we were used to.

We told that to our parents, but they explained to us that because Abba was offered a good job in Yerushalayim, one that matched his talents, we had no other option.

Slowly but surely, we kids realized that there was no choice, but we still felt sad about it.

We said goodbye to our friends, each of us in his own way. For instance, I made a going-away party, where I gave each kid a note and a small gift. My sister Tali didn't want any party. She just told everyone at the end of the year that we were moving, and that was it as far as she was concerned. She explained to us that she was like Tzviki Green in your book, Mr. Walder. She didn't like goodbyes, so she preferred not to celebrate them.

My mother said it sounded like she was running away from reality instead of coping with it, to which Tali replied, "Could be. So what?"

*   *   *

We packed up the house, and one day in the middle of this past Av, a big truck arrived at our house. Within an hour and a half, the movers had taken everything our parents and us kids had collected over many years and loaded it onto their truck.

We traveled in our car. (You're probably curious to know if everyone rides in the moving van when you move. So the answer is no. The moving van is just for your things. People move by car.)

On the way, the mood was gloomy. Abba tried to lift the tension by playing music or talking, but we weren't so into it. When I looked around, I saw tears on my brothers' and sisters' faces, and when I touched my own eyes, I realized that they saw the same thing on my face.

We arrived in Yerushalayim, and to tell you the truth, I was pleasantly surprised because the new apartment was bigger than our old one, and the view was amazing and reminded me a little of the magical atmosphere of Tzefas. We were busy unpacking and setting things up in the house, so our days were busy and I didn't have too much time to think. Before we knew it, Elul arrived.

I went to a new school, to a new class, with boys I didn't know.

*   *   *

When I arrived in the classroom, I felt pretty miserable. There were thirty kids there I'd never seen before. They knew I was a new kid, but they didn't know what to say or how to welcome me.

I had to face thirty pairs of eyes staring at me with curiosity. It wasn't all that pleasant.

Luckily, the teacher came in, told everyone to sit,

and said, "Welcome to sixth grade." Then he added, "There's a new boy here. His name is Yoni, and he came from Tzefas. Yoni, can you tell us a little bit about what it's like to live in Tzefas?"

I turned red as thirty kids looked at me again. I said something like, "Fine, *baruch Hashem.*" I knew I hadn't really answered his question, but he didn't press me, and the lesson began.

I tried to concentrate but wasn't able to. I felt completely out of place, in a place I didn't know, with kids I didn't know. I thought about how hard it was for me to be in this situation, where they'd taken me from the place I'd grown up in and from my friends and put me here.

I had tears in my eyes, so I rested my head on my arms so no one would see.

At recess, I went outside to the schoolyard. I saw everyone busy with his own interests. A few kids asked me my name, as if they hadn't heard it from the teacher, and a few of them told me their names even though I didn't ask. Only one boy was friendly and said, "You'll like it here. And if you have any problems, I'm here." He spoke like a man of thirty.

School ended. I ran home and burst into tears as soon as I opened the door.

"What happened?" my mother asked as she came toward me.

"Nothing happened," I said to her. "I don't know a single kid there. I'm in a strange place, and I don't have anything to do here, and I want to go back to Tzefas."

As if that wasn't enough, my sister Tali came home right then, tears streaming down her face, and ran to her room. She didn't even go to the trouble of saying what happened. She just buried her head in her pillow and didn't want to talk.

What can I say? The house was like Tishah B'Av. The little kids came home from nursery school and pre-1A happy as could be as if it was the place they'd been going to forever. They excitedly told us how much fun they'd had and what great new friends they had.

My mother explained to us later that the little kids had just moved from one kindergarten to another, just like most kids their age. Also, they didn't see moving from one place to another as anything special. Maybe they thought everyone was like them.

*   *   *

A few more days went by and nothing improved. I felt very down and dragged myself to school each day. I missed my Tzefas friends a lot. When I looked at the boys in my class, I couldn't see myself being friends with a single one of them.

On Thursday when I came home, Abba and Ima were waiting to have a talk with me.

"Look," my father said, "I understand you're in a new place, and you don't exactly connect. I want you to tell me what you're feeling."

"I look at the boys here, but none of them are as interesting as Avichai or David or Moshe or my other friends in Tzefas," I said. "They're just boring kids. We've got nothing in common, and I'm never going to get used to it."

I started crying bitterly.

"What makes you think they're not your type?" my father asked.

"I know."

"Did you talk to them?"

"I've got nothing to talk to them about."

"Look, Yoni," my father explained, "I'm certain that out of thirty boys, there are at least ten who are interesting, fascinating, friendly, and funny just like the boys in your class in Tzefas. But if you never talk to them, you'll never find that out."

"So, why do I feel this way?"

"Because right now, they really are strangers to you.

None of them look like Moshe or Avichai or David, but in their thinking and emotions there will be many who are like them and perhaps even more suited to you than the boys in Tzefas were. If you don't try to make friends, you'll never know."

My father suggested that I stop looking so miserable and instead try to reach out even with simple things like asking, "Can I borrow your pencil?" or "Where's the principal's office?" (even if I already had a pencil and even if I knew where the principal's office was. Just connect).

With no choice, I began to try.

I went over to Shloimi, the boy who had talked to me on the first day of school, and asked him, "Where is the principal's office?" He got all excited and ran to show me where the office was. We walked together, and he asked me, "Do you like it here?"

"The truth?" I said to him. "I didn't get used to it yet."

"Of course not," he said. "You still don't know the boys here. You haven't talked to anyone in the class. Are you shy or something?"

"I'm not exactly shy," I explained, "but it's hard for me to connect right now."

"That's okay," he said. "Take your time."

*   *   *

A few days passed, and, as they say, I took my time. But still, nothing.

I got into some bad thoughts. Not only about my situation but even the helplessness I was in. I felt that I was suffering from the move more than anyone else in our family, that they had separated me from my best and closest friends, and that no one could help me. I decided I had to help myself.

And then a strange thought entered my mind. A type of thought I'd never ever had before.

I decided that since no one cared about me and I was so lonesome and miserable, I would just return to Tzefas by myself and go back to my class and my friends.

It took me a day or two to come to a decision, and when I'd more or less decided to go through with it, I remembered one very important detail.

The trip to Tzefas cost money. Where would I get around fifty shekels?

In the past, I'd ask my mother for the money.

I could do the same now, but I knew very well that she'd ask me, "What do you need it for?" That's the question every parent asks. Parents don't just give their kids money. That's not good *chinuch*.

I'm not one to lie to my parents, so I struggled with the problem of how to get the money. I did most of my thinking during class. I was so absorbed in my thoughts that I didn't even hear the bell ring or see everyone leave for recess.

*   *   *

Suddenly, someone interrupted me while I was making plans.

"Okay, so you're daydreaming in class. But you'll probably be better off going outside for recess so you'll have something to dream about in the next class."

It was Shloimi.

"I didn't hear the bell ring," I told him. "I was really deep in thought."

"Now I'm curious," Shloimi said. "What are you thinking about so much?"

"Uh…" I was hesitant to let him know. "Actually, I wanted to ask your advice."

"You're coming to the right person," Shloimi said. "I'm an expert at it." He sounded like the school guidance counselor. "Talk."

"Do you know how I can get around fifty shekels?"

"Fifty shekels? What do you need fifty shekels for?"

If I'd had any hope that my mother might skip that question, I'd just gotten proof that she wouldn't.

"I'll tell you the truth. Don't feel bad, but I don't really relate to the kids here in this class. My parents decided to move, and I was forced to leave my class and friends behind. I want to go back to Tzefas, to my school and my friends."

His eyes grew round with surprise. "But where will you sleep? Where will you eat?"

That was nice of him. He skipped over the *really* hard questions, like, "What will your parents say and where will you stay?" Those were good points. He didn't criticize the plan. He just took an interest in how I'd pull it off.

"My uncle and aunt live there so I can sleep at their house." I hadn't arranged anything with them, but I was certain they wouldn't close the door in my face. "The only problem is that I don't have any money."

"Listen," he said, "I totally get you, but I have only twenty-six shekels. Do you mind if I tell a few other friends and ask them to help you?"

I wasn't quick to answer. I felt a little ashamed. *They didn't know me, but I was already asking them for money?*

"I'm not so comfortable with that. And I didn't ask

you for money. You just surprised me by asking what I was thinking about. I don't know how the other kids would look at it."

"Don't worry," he said. "I think they'll be excited about it actually. You can relax. Give me a few minutes."

He left the classroom and came back within five minutes with another three friends.

They sat down across from me and started to do some fundraising among themselves.

"Uh, I don't think fifty shekels is enough," a boy named Yoel said. "You need at least one hundred shekels so you'll have money to come back." (I'd never even considered the matter of "coming back.")

"And what about cola and falafel?" probed Shmulik (who definitely looked like someone who knew a thing or two about cola and falafel).

They started to promise specific amounts. Shloimi promised his twenty-six shekels. Two boys promised thirty each. And the fourth boy said he had twenty for sure, but his sister owed him another twenty, and he'd ask her if she could pay him back or if she was planning to run away to Tzefas. Everyone laughed. Actually, I did too.

In the end, they collected one hundred and thirty shekels, which included money for a cola and falafel and extra "just in case you need it." They all promised to bring candy and snacks to help me make it through the trip. Shloimi and another friend named Motty gave me their home phone numbers so I could let them know when I arrived, to make sure I hadn't gotten lost. Those kids had thought of everything.

It was decided that the trip would take place the following week on Sunday.

"It's best if you go back there at the beginning of the week," Shloimi said.

"And besides," a different kid said, "you'll need Shabbos to rest up and eat a lot before you travel."

I don't need to tell you who said that.

Together, these four boys and I planned every last detail of the trip—at which bus stop I'd board the bus and at what time (one o'clock, when everyone went home for lunch), what I'd wear, what I'd put in my backpack, and of course, what food I'd take along.

At a certain point, other kids in the class sensed that something was going on, but the boys who were helping me told them that it was private. They'd decided among themselves not to talk about it so there wouldn't be any way word of the plan could leak.

We shook hands on it and waited for Sunday.

*　*　*

I was fairly tense over Shabbos but also looking forward to my trip. It was clear to me that if I did what I planned, my parents would regret their decision to move and would return to Tzefas. And if not, I'd just stay there at my aunt and uncle's house and be with my friends.

Sunday arrived. I came with my backpack. At recess, kids brought me all sorts of food and snacks. Close to one o'clock, Shloimi came over with money in a thin wallet they'd gotten somehow.

"Put this in your pocket and guard it carefully," he said. "We'll walk you to the bus stop after school and make sure you get on the right bus."

School ended. We walked together, five boys, toward the bus stop.

I was feeling great. These boys were turning out to be really good friends. They were helping me, giving me advice, giving me their support. They'd even given me their own money that they'd saved. I couldn't help but appreciate that. The closer we got to the bus stop, the more a certain thought kept bothering me. I suddenly got cold feet (that's an expression that means I was having second thoughts about what I'd planned to do), but I pushed it aside. I have no idea why. I think I felt uncomfortable since my new friends had gone to so much trouble for me. How could I just back out now?

They were cheerful and happy and kept warning me to make sure to call and tell them what was going on.

"Call me every night," Shloimi said.

"Why just you?" Yoel asked. "Call me, too."

An argument began, and in the end it was decided that every day I'd call a different boy and he'd report to the others.

And then the bus pulled up at the stop.

"That's it!" the boys stood up and exclaimed excitedly. "The great escape begins."

I didn't feel well at all, but I didn't say anything. I started walking toward the bus and was glad for the long line. I hoped the driver would announce that there was no room, but that didn't happen. People boarded the bus, and in another moment it would be my turn.

"You know something?" Shloimi said. "You look pale."

"Yeah," I said. "I don't feel good."

"It'll pass," Shmulik said. "Eat something and—"

"No," Shloimi interrupted. "He really doesn't look good." Then to me, he said, "No big deal. Wait for the next bus. It's supposed to come in thirty minutes. We'll wait with you."

The bus drove off, and I breathed a sigh of relief.

*   *   *

They started talking to pass the time, and then Shloimi said to me, "So, do you feel better now?"

"Yes," I said, "but not because of what you're all thinking."

"What are we all thinking?"

"You're thinking that I'm waiting for the next bus, but I hereby announce to everyone that I'm not waiting for another bus. I've decided to stay here."

They couldn't believe it. "Why?"

"Do you know why I wanted to go back?"

"Sure we do," Yoel said. "You miss your friends, and you didn't make any new friends. That's what you told us."

"So that's just it. I did find new friends—you," I said. "Believe me, I really do miss my friends in Tzefas. After my parents decided to move, I was sure I'd never find friends like the ones I'd had. But these last few days showed me that I've found friends no less good than the ones I had. You're really true friends. You're so kind, such great kids. You care, and you know how to keep a secret. So I decided that it's not so urgent for me to go to Tzefas."

No one said a word. I looked at their faces. I was afraid they'd be disappointed that the plan of my escape wasn't happening. But I was wrong. They looked pleased.

"Actually," Shloimi said, "I thought about it last night, and I said to myself, 'Too bad Yoni doesn't see what great, trustworthy friends he has here.' But I was embarrassed to say that to you, so I told myself, 'Yoni doesn't think so. He's still attached to his old friends.' I'm happy you discovered the truth."

And what is the truth, you're probably wondering?

Actually, though I was very close with my friends in Tzefas, and I still think of them and stay in touch with them, I found out that you can find friends anywhere if you just open your eyes and if you don't get discouraged. That's what I found out last year during Elul.

What I discovered personally I want to share with all the kids who are starting school or who moved to a different school: Don't get discouraged. Don't think your social life is over. Pay attention to my story. I feel like shouting out its key points. All you need to do is open your eyes, look for new friends, connect with them.

What happened to me was a kind of miracle. As I was running away from my friends, I found them.

The Rebbe's Kippah of Peace

My name is Aryeh Leib.

I'm twelve, and I live in Yerushalayim.

Our family is Chassidic. We have a Rebbe who leads us, and we try our best to follow his guidelines.

A year ago, I started to feel unwell. At first, my parents thought it was the flu or some virus. But when I started to feel worse, the doctor sent me for more tests, and that's how they found out I had cancer.

You've probably heard of this illness. It's considered one of the most difficult because it's life-threatening if it's not treated.

Naturally, my parents took me to top doctors. They decided that I needed to get something called chemotherapy. "Chemo" means a chemical substance, and "therapy" means healing. The chemical substance was supposed to cure the disease and heal me.

Before they started the treatment, they explained it to me.

They explained that chemotherapy is a strong substance that kills the cancerous cells, which is great. The problem is that it also harms the body a little because it hurts the healthy parts, too. They told me that I would feel weak and even *very* weak. They said there would even be times when it would be forbidden for me to be close to other people so that I wouldn't get infected from their germs. But in the end, the chemo would beat the cancer, *b'ezras Hashem*, and I would go back to being a regular healthy child.

I understood what they were saying and thought to myself that it was worth it to suffer a little to beat the illness and be well again.

Then the doctor said, "There's something else. There will be times when you'll be bald."

I looked at him and didn't know why he thought this was big news. "I'm always bald. I don't understand what you're telling me."

The doctor was taken aback, and my parents began to laugh.

They explained to the doctor that Chassidic boys always cut their hair very short, so for me, going bald would only save me the time it took to go to the barber.

Once the doctor understood, he also started laughing, and said, "Okay. I don't know if it'll look exactly the same, but if it's okay for you, great."

That's what he said.

*   *   *

A week later, I started treatment. I was getting a medicine they give once a week.

At first, I didn't feel anything. But a week later, I started to understand what the doctor meant. I began to feel weak and nauseous. I threw up a lot, and my whole body became weaker. The more medicine I got, the worse I felt.

At first, I was an outpatient. That means you come into the hospital in the morning, they give you medicine until the afternoon, and then you go home.

Eventually, they had to keep me in the hospital overnight, too. That's because my body got so weak that I needed close medical supervision.

Every time I went to the hospital, I'd see the same kids in the unit who had the same illness as I did, and they looked just like me, bald and weak, but we hardly had anything to do with each other.

Once I started staying overnight, though, I got to know them more because we were in the hospital all

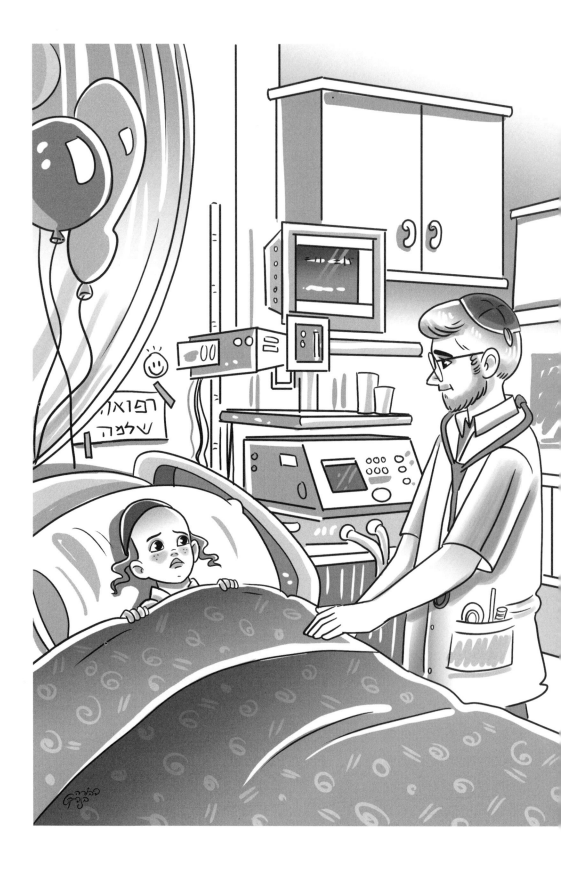

day and all night, so it was only natural to become more familiar with the other kids there.

That's how I met Elkanah.

Elkanah was a religious boy like I am, but he wasn't Chassidic. He had a knitted *kippah* on his head. My father explained to me that he belonged to a different religious group and that his family has their own rabbi.

Somehow we were in the hospital together a lot. Once in a while, we talked to each other.

I remember one time when I felt awful, and he said to me, "It's okay. I feel like that sometimes, too, but it goes away."

I thanked him, and that's how we started talking.

He told me that the hardest thing for him was losing his hair. I told him that that was the least hard thing for me because I go like that all the time anyway.

"Are you making fun of me?" he said.

"We chassidim laugh at someone who goes with a *'chup.'*"

"What's a *chup*?"

"A *chup* is a *bloreet*."

"What's a *bloreet*?"

"Nu, it's what you have," I told him. "You know, the hairstyle you used to have when you had hair you could comb."

"Hold it," he said. "Are you saying you don't comb your hair?"

"I'm saying that I have no hair to comb, because the minute our hair grows even a little, we go to a barber so we'll look the way we should."

I saw him fall silent as he tried to picture it, and suddenly, both of us were laughing.

"Actually, I do comb my hair," I said.

"How can you comb a bald head?" he asked, and we laughed again.

"Not the bald head. I comb my *peyos*."

"Oh, right," he said. "But…how come your *peyos* didn't fall out?"

"Well, these aren't really my *peyos*," I said. "It's synthetic hair that my parents bought me. I put it on either side of my head, and it looks like *peyos*." (It was really a secret that I hadn't told a single person, including my brothers and sisters. But I didn't mind telling Elkanah, maybe because he was bald, too.)

"I don't believe it," Elkanah said. "Show me."

I hesitated a little, and then I lifted my *kippah* and showed him the hairs that were stretched across my head from side to side. The *kippah* covered it so that it looked real.

"Wow!" Elkanah said. "It's like a *peah* of *peyos*."

"I don't get it."

"They suggested that I get a *peah*—you know, a wig—to replace the hair. I wore one for a little while, but it bothered me. I'd rather go around like this. For you, they made *peyos* out of a *peah*."

It was a cute idea, and we laughed again.

* * *

Two days later, we were released and sent home. I continued the treatment as an outpatient, but a month and a half later, my medical situation got a little complicated when I caught a very dangerous virus. I was hospitalized again.

I was in the hospital for a week and released before Yom Kippur.

On Yom Kippur, I was very, very weak and wasn't allowed to fast (I'm not obligated yet anyway), and on *motza'ei Yom Kippur*, before I went back to the hospital, my father took me to the Rebbe.

It's not easy to get in to see the Rebbe. Actually, children younger than bar mitzvah don't go in to see the Rebbe at all (they see him in the enormous *beis medrash* and even wish him a *Gut Shabbos*, but only adults go into the Rebbe's room).

But because I was sick, I was given a privilege that

all my brothers envied (and that's not the only privilege I was given...).

The Rebbe is a tzaddik in his seventies, and he is the leader of tens of thousands of chassidim. I felt very excited but also a little bit scared.

The Rebbe asked me (in Yiddish) how I felt, and I said to him, "*Baruch Hashem*, better." He asked me if I was in contact with my friends and I answered that a few of them came to visit me, whenever they could. He asked if people were spoiling me with candy, and I said yes.

And then the Rebbe said to me, "I am davening for you to be healthy. All Rosh Hashanah and also on Yom Kippur, I davened for you, and all the chassidim are davening for you and wish you a speedy *refuah sheleimah*."

Tears came to my eyes.

The Rebbe shook my hand, and I was about to leave when he said, "One minute."

He whispered a few words to his assistant (by us, he's called the *shamash*). The *shamash* looked very surprised and even asked, "Really?" and the Rebbe confirmed it, and then the *shamash* went over to a nearby closet and took a big white *kippah* out of it.

"This is the *kippah* I wore on Rosh Hashanah and

Yom Kippur," the Rebbe told me. "If you wish, you can wear it when you don't feel well, and maybe it will improve the way you feel."

I looked at my father. He was amazed. No one gets the Rebbe's *kippah*, certainly not the one he wore on Yom Kippur. It was the biggest present I could have gotten.

We went straight from there to the hospital. I was wearing the Rebbe's *kippah*.

* * *

When we got to the room, who did I find there but Elkanah.

He had been hospitalized before Yom Kippur. His condition wasn't that great either. We also had a third friend in the room. Sayid was two years younger than we were. He didn't have any *kippah*, and actually, he wasn't Jewish. He lived in one of the villages near Yerushalayim. Elkanah knew him because they'd already been there together for a few days.

We talked a little. Each of us told the others what he'd gone through during the past month. And then Elkanah asked me, "Did you change your *kippah*?"

"No. Why should I?"

I took off the Rebbe's *kippah* so Elkanah could see

that underneath it, I was wearing my own *kippah*.

"So what's that? A *kippah* on a *kippah* on a *peyah* of a *peah*?"

We rolled with laughter. Sayid didn't understand a word, even though he knew Hebrew. Elkanah explained it to him.

*   *   *

We went to sleep, and the next day the three of us underwent treatment that, as usual, left us feeling weak.

We lay there silently for hours and hours. We slept a lot and then woke up when it was already nighttime.

Elkanah's mother didn't come, and my mother didn't come either. I saw that he didn't feel good, so I brought him a glass of water and sat next to him.

"I really don't feel good," he said. "I'm scared."

"It'll be okay," I told him. "Everyone says we're going to get better."

"Easy for you to say," Elchanan said. "You have the Rebbe's *kippah*, so you're going to get better."

I thought about that and then said, "I don't mind lending you the Rebbe's *kippah* to wear."

"Do you really mean that?"

"Sure," I said to him. "I wear it all the time, and I

have a *kippah* under it, so why shouldn't you benefit from it, too?"

Elkanah could hardly believe it when I took off the Rebbe's *kippah* and put it on his head.

"Could I sleep a little with the *kippah*?" Elkanah asked.

"Sure," I said. "Give it back to me in the morning."

Elkanah rested his head on the pillow and instantly fell asleep.

And so did I.

In the morning, I opened my eyes to see Elkanah standing there next to my bed.

"You know what?" he said. "This *kippah* really works. I feel a lot better."

"Of course you do," I said. "It's my Rebbe's."

"Who's your Rebbe?" Elkanah asked. "What's his name?"

"We don't say our Rebbe's name, the same way we don't say our father's name," I said.

"So what do you call him?"

"Simple. 'The Rebbe.' The same way you say 'Abba.'"

"Oh," Elkanah said. "Can you explain to me what chassidim are?"

"I'll try, but it's a long story. Do you have the strength to listen?"

"Sure!" Elkanah said.

"I'd like to know too," said Sayid.

I began telling them.

*   *   *

About three hundred and fifty years ago (I told Elkanah and Sayid), the Jewish people in Europe went through very hard times. Back then, there weren't many Jews here in Eretz Yisrael. They were spread out all over the world, mostly in Europe and the Arab countries.

In the Arab countries, Jews were usually treated well, and in most places, hardly anything bad happened to them. But in Christian Europe, the situation was different. They always found excuses to expel the Jews and steal their property and possessions. Even worse, mobs would often kill them and burn their homes.

After hundreds of years of terrible suffering and persecution by the Inquisition and then the Cossacks and all sorts of rioters, the Jewish people in Europe were on the brink of despair. They were suffering so much, they felt they didn't have any strength left. They were poor and downtrodden and just prayed for Mashiach to come.

And then a man named Shabbetai Tzvi appeared. He told everyone he was Mashiach. He fooled many people into believing him, and they became his followers. They were sure he would bring an end to their suffering.

But after a few years, people found out that he was a liar and a cheat. The Jewish people were devastated and felt like there was no more hope. They sank deeper and deeper into despair.

Many individuals learned Torah, and there were great Torah scholars, but for the most part, the masses didn't know how to learn Torah.

Then the Baal Shem Tov was born.

He went from village to village telling Jews, "Hashem loves you. You don't have to know how to learn or to be a Torah scholar. He loves you even if you don't know how to read. All you need to do is believe in Hashem, do mitzvos, and be happy that He chose you to be His children. You'll see that He will return your strength to you."

The downtrodden people were very relieved that this special man believed in them so much. He taught them that there are many ways to speak to Hashem and that a person can speak to Him with the words that are in his heart. He taught them that it's possible to be happy and sing and through that become close to Hashem. He gave them warmth and love. After so many years of being oppressed and humiliated, they felt proud to be Jews again. Gradually a group of people became his followers and called him "Rabbi Yisrael Baal Shem Tov."

He was the founder of Chassidus.

This movement saved so many Jews. People began doing mitzvos with joy and later began learning Torah and Chassidus.

What was important to Rabbi Yisrael was that they not change their own special language. He told people to speak *lashon kodesh*, to keep their Jewish names, and not to change their dress but to keep the Jewish look, with a beard and *peyos*.

In Egypt, the Jews guarded their Jewishness by not changing their names, language, or dress, and the chassidim guarded their Jewishness the same way. Disciples of the Baal Shem Tov, people who had learned his teachings, became leaders and gathered around them many other Jews, who called themselves chassidim. Chassidim believe that a tzaddik can guide them and strengthen their connection to Hashem.

At first, some people were afraid of the Baal Shem Tov's teachings and were opposed to Chassidus. But

over the years, they saw how successful it was in bringing Jews close to Torah, in preserving the Jewish look
of a beard and *peyos*, and in strengthening people's
love of Hashem and love of doing mitzvos, so they
stopped being opposed to Chassidus, and it's now an
important part of the Jewish people.

* * *

"That's an amazing story you just told us," Elkanah
said.

"What a great story," Sayid agreed.

I hadn't planned on telling them a story. I'd just
wanted to explain what Chassidus is.

"I'm still not finished," I said.

* * *

A student of the Baal Shem Tov called Rabbi
Elimelech of Lizhensk had a student who was called the
Chozeh of Lublin. *His* student, Rabbi Shalom Rokeach,
founded our Chassidus two hundred years ago.

When Rabbi Shalom died, his son Rabbi Yehoshua
Rokeach became the Rebbe. Then *his* son Rabbi
Yissachar Dov became the Rebbe. When he died, his
son, Rabbi Aharon Rokeach, became the Rebbe.

By now, over one hundred years had passed, and

the small group of chassidim had become a very large Chassidus of tens of thousands of chassidim who lived in Poland and the Ukraine. Everything thrived because they took care of each other like family. It was their own small kingdom.

Then the terrible Holocaust came and erased everything.

Almost everything.

Tens of thousands of chassidim with their wives and children were killed when the evil Nazis slaughtered European Jewry.

The chassidim realized that everything they'd built was going to be wiped out. They decided that the most important thing was to save the Rebbe because they were afraid that if he was killed, the Chassidus would end.

You have no idea what they did to save him. They paid people a lot of money to hide him and keep him safe until eventually, they managed to get him out of Poland and into Hungary, to safety. The chassidim, who parted from him in tears, knew that their own fate was doomed, but it gave them joy and satisfaction to know that the dynasty would continue.

The Rebbe came to Eretz Yisrael and reestablished the Chassidus. But of all the tens of thousands of followers, only a few dozen were left. He was so sad about the loss of so many wonderful Jews that it broke his heart, and he died of grief.

Our Chassidus was about to disappear.

But this Rebbe had a little son. A nine-year-old boy. What would happen now? Some of the elderly chassidim who had survived said, "He may be only nine, but that's a defect that will pass. He will grow up, and we will crown him Rebbe."

Many people thought it was a dream that would never come true, but it did.

The boy was educated from childhood to grow in holiness and purity, to learn Torah, and how to lead the Chassidus. He had the best teachers, who not only taught him Torah but also who his ancestors were. That's how he grew up when the Chassidus had no leader.

When he got married, his wedding was the biggest Chassidic wedding since the Holocaust. Even many people who weren't part of our Chassidus came to see it. For them, this was the way to rejoice that the Holocaust had failed to destroy the Jewish people.

A year and a half after he married, all the chassidim who had waited so many years for him, crowned him the Rebbe.

My father wasn't even born then, but my

grandfather was twelve when it happened. He knew that he belonged to the Chassidus and had been looking forward to the crowning of the Rebbe for many years. Even now, when he tells us about it, his eyes sparkle.

My grandfather says that many people outside of the Chassidus didn't believe the young Rebbe could restore the Chassidus to what it once was. Some even laughed at the chassidim who had waited so many years for a child of nine to grow up. But our chassidim didn't pay any attention to what those people said. It was important to them to restore the Chassidus to what it was. That would be the answer to the evil Nazis.

* * *

The young Rebbe began to lead a small group of people. Though most were older than he was, they accepted his authority. All were waiting for him to have a son to continue the Chassidus.

But the Rebbe did not have any children. A year passed, then five years, and then eight, and still no children. The chassidim were very sad. They'd done so much to continue the dynasty, to save the Rebbe, to raise him and prepare him from the age of nine to become their leader. What would happen now?

And then, after a ten-year wait, when all the chassidim had nearly given up, a miracle took place: A son was born to the Rebbe and his wife.

I can't even begin to describe to you what went on then. By then, my grandfather was twenty-two, married, and the father of one child (my father). He says that the minute the good news became public, even before the bris and everything, all the chassidim got dressed in their holiday clothes (meaning, a *kapote* and *shtreimel*) and traveled to Yerushalayim.

"I've never experienced such joy in my life as I did then, and I don't think I ever will until the day I die," is how my grandfather described what it felt like when an heir was born to our Rebbe. "Thousands of people were dancing, their eyes red from tears of joy, gratitude, and relief. Thousands of people joined in the dancing because they knew that our Chassidus would now continue."

I can tell you that by now the Rebbe's only son already has more than ten children, which means that we no longer have to worry about the continuation of our Chassidus. But the Rebbe still continues to lead us, and he is so wise and such a tzaddik, that he has turned our Chassidus into a real empire with tens of thousands of followers who obey his every word. He cares about every one of us, about our health and if we have enough money, and he cares about every single Jew.

On Rosh Hashanah and Yom Kippur, the Rebbe is the chazzan in his shul which is the biggest in the whole world and can be seen from all over Yerushalayim, and he wears a white *kittel* (instead of the usual black clothes) and on his head is a white *kippah* made from last year's *kittel*.

So now do you understand what happened here? *That's* the *kippah* he gave me to make me feel better and become healthy.

*   *   *

I began to cry and saw that Elkanah and Sayid were crying with me.

Suddenly we noticed that we were not alone. Our fathers stood some distance away, listening to my fascinating story. My father, Elkanah's father, and Sayid's father had all covered their eyes with their hands, probably because they were embarrassed about crying.

The three of us went to get our treatments, and then we came back to rest. We were all very tired.

*   *   *

When we woke up in the afternoon, Elkanah

started asking me a lot of questions. I tried to answer him as best I could. He wanted to know more about what a Rebbe is and what chassidim are, and what a *tish* is (that's the Yiddish word for the table the Rebbe presides over every Shabbos night; after having their regular Shabbos meal at home, the chassidim return to the Rebbe's table, where they celebrate together), and what a *kvitel* is (it's a note with your name written on it so the Rebbe can bless you).

Then, out of the blue, Sayid asked me, "Can I wear this *kippah* of the Rebbe too?"

Elkanah and I looked at each other. We didn't know what to answer. Sayid wasn't a Jew. Would it be okay to let him wear the Rebbe's *kippah*?

Elkanah tried to save the situation. "I think we'd need to ask the Rebbe's permission," he said in an authoritative tone.

"But Aryeh Leib let you wear it without asking permission," Sayid replied.

I'd never been in such an uncomfortable position in my life. What should I say to Sayid? What should I do?

Since I didn't know what to do, I decided to think about the Rebbe. What would *he* do in such a situation? As soon as I thought about it, I knew immediately what he *wouldn't* do.

My Rebbe wouldn't embarrass anyone. He wouldn't hurt anyone, whether he was Jewish or not. That was one hundred percent clear to me.

I said to Sayid, "You're right. My Rebbe would certainly agree to let you wear it."

I removed the *kippah* from my head and placed it on Sayid's head.

With the big white *kippah* covering nearly his whole head, Sayid said, "Thanks. Now I'm sure I'll recover."

Two hours later, before we went to bed, Sayid returned the *kippah* to me. I was happy to have it back, but I was worried. Maybe I hadn't done the right thing? Maybe it was forbidden to give the *kippah* to someone who wasn't Jewish?

I didn't dare tell my thoughts to my mother, who'd come to stay with me. I just fell asleep.

* * *

A few months passed, and one day there was a doctors' conference with me and my parents at which my primary physician happily informed us that I was in full remission. It was over. I was now healthy and could return to normal life.

My father and mother hugged me and thanked the doctors for being trustworthy agents of Hashem to heal me. They also gave them gifts to show their appreciation.

"It wasn't only us," my doctor said. "It was the Rebbe's *kippah*. Everyone who wore it got better."

My parents were happy to hear that, and my father said, "That reminds me. I need to return the *kippah* to the Rebbe."

We left, and after a lot of hesitation, I said to my father, "I want to return the *kippah* to the Rebbe myself."

"It's not so acceptable," he told me. "When you were sick, it was one thing. But now you're healthy, and children your age don't go in to see the Rebbe.

"Tell the *shamash* that I'm asking to go in to see the Rebbe to return the *kippah* and that there's something very important I need to ask him."

My father looked at me in surprise. I saw that he was debating whether to ask me what I was planning to ask the Rebbe, but he decided not to.

Two days later, my father informed me that the Rebbe would be happy to have me come.

I was very nervous about this meeting. At the appointed hour, we entered the room to see the Rebbe. My father stood in the corner of the huge room so I could approach the Rebbe in a way that no one would hear what we were saying.

I took out the white *kippah* and put it on the table. Then I said, "Rebbe, I have a question. Is it okay that I let some other sick children wear the *kippah*?"

"*Avada, avada* (certainly, certainly)," the Rebbe said. "What's the question?"

"But Rebbe, one of those children wasn't Jewish. He asked me for the *kippah,* and I didn't want to hurt his feelings."

Suddenly I saw the Rebbe crying. He held my head in his two hands and said, "A *teiyereh yingele* (a precious child). A *yingele tzadikel* (a tzaddik of a boy). You did the right thing. That's how a Jew should act."

The Rebbe signaled my father to come closer and said to him, "How did you merit to have a child like this? How did I merit to have a chassid who has a child like this?"

Then the Rebbe said, "Do you know what they called the founder of our Chassidus? 'Rabbi Shalom.' That was his name, and that was his path in life, the path of peace. Jews were never raised to hate. The gentiles were always raised to hate us. The path of our first Rebbe, Dov Ber Shalom, was always one of *derech eretz* and never to hurt anyone."

Then the Rebbe took the white *kippah* and handed it to me. "I think the best place for this *kippah* is with you.

I am giving it to you as a gift, and may you be healthy and blessed with generations and raise them this way. This *kippah* will remain with you so that you will tell the whole world how a Jewish child must behave."

And that's what I'm doing now, telling this story to children everywhere. It's the story of "The Rebbe's *Kippah* of Peace."

"Wolf!"

My name is Dudi.

I'm twelve, and I'm in seventh grade. I live in Beitar Illit.

The story I want to tell you happened to our class recently.

We were all sitting in our seats, not paying too much attention to the lesson, and even whispering among ourselves. Behind me sat a boy named Motty. That day, Motty brought a snuffbox with him.

If you don't know what a snuffbox is, then you're not a Yerushalmi. (I myself don't live in Yerushalayim, but Yerushalayim isn't only a place, it's also a type.) Anyway, in every Yerushalmi shul, there are a few people who bring a small container of tobacco called "snuff" that has a very pleasant aroma, and they give everyone who wants, a pinch of snuff to smell.

Children don't have their own snuffboxes, but they're offered the snuff from the adults' snuff boxes. Usually, the snuffboxes are made of silver, and the person who has a snuffbox feels like the richest person in the world.

That day Motty came to school with his father's snuffbox. We didn't ask him if his father had given him the snuffbox or if he had taken it without permission. I think kids prefer not to ask questions whose answers aren't worth knowing.

What was worth it to us was taking turns with Motty's snuffbox, so we preferred not to ask unnecessary questions.

It was mint-flavored tobacco, sharp but pleasant, and we all started sneezing as the snuff tickled our nose. For every pinch of snuff Motty offered us, he took two pinches for himself. The tobacco isn't dangerous if you take a pinch, but it *is* dangerous if you take twenty pinches. We didn't pay attention to how many pinches of snuff Motty took, because what business was it of ours?

All of a sudden, Motty whispered to Yossi, who was sitting next to him, "I think I'm going to faint."

* * *

Before I continue the story, I have to mention here that Motty knows how to put on a good act. He can pretend he's falling, and then, when everyone comes rushing over in a panic to help him, he'll laugh and say, "The joke's on you." So you can see why Yossi started laughing.

"Are you tricking me again?" he said to Motty.

But Motty said, "It's not a trick. I'm really going to faint."

Yossi didn't believe him because after someone's pretended a hundred times to faint as a joke, you don't believe him anymore. So he decided to test him.

"Do you want me to tell the teacher?" Yossi asked. He was certain Motty would say, "Are you crazy? It was a joke."

But Motty said, "Yes. Tell the teacher."

Yossi still didn't believe him, but why not have some fun? He told the teacher.

At first, the teacher didn't pay too much attention because he also knew Motty and his acting ability. But when Motty whispered to Yossi again that he was going to faint, Yossi noticed that Motty looked pale and he was crying.

"What's the matter?" Yossi whispered to him.

Motty tried to talk but he couldn't, so Yossi ran to

the teacher and told him that it was for real, that Motty was about to faint.

The teacher took one look at Motty and realized it was no game. The whole class watched as Motty's eyes rolled up, and he fainted. The teacher rushed over and caught him just in time.

*   *   *

The teacher told me to call my father, who also teaches in our school and knows first aid.

I raced to my father. He was in the middle of helping students board the school bus safely, so he sent a different teacher who had also learned first aid.

We ran together to the classroom. By now, Motty lay on the floor unconscious, and the whole class stood around him nervously. The teacher lifted Motty's legs and told two children to hold them up high. The scene was very frightening.

With the whole class watching, the teacher checked to see if Motty was breathing. Then he told us, "It's okay. He just fainted. Step back a little to give him some air."

Someone brought a glass of water and wiped Motty's face. We watched as Motty slowly opened his eyes. We were all very worried.

The teacher told Motty to drink, but right then Motty threw up. I don't want to describe what he looked like after sniffing so much snuff. It wasn't good for him. He finally drank some water and slowly got back to himself.

The teacher called his parents, and Motty's mother asked if they could bring him to the gate. The teacher lifted him in his arms, just like a baby, because Motty couldn't walk on his own, and didn't even notice all his friends surrounding him with worried looks on their faces.

Within five minutes, his mother arrived in a taxi and took him to the nearest health clinic. We ran after the taxi, and when we caught up to it, Motty was still inside. His mother was waiting for someone to bring a wheelchair so she could take him in. A nurse came out, and when she saw Motty's face, she said to his mother, "This isn't something for the clinic. You need to take him to the hospital."

They ordered an ambulance.

Motty's mother seemed anxious. "What happened?" she asked. "Who gave him so much tobacco?!"

We didn't answer her. How could we tattle on a friend who had just fainted? What should we say to her, that he himself brought the tobacco to school?

That he took two pinches for himself for every pinch he gave us? That he sniffed it into his nose as hard as he could and breathed it deep into his lungs?

We decided not to say any of that, and to make sure we moved away so that she wouldn't ask us again, and we wouldn't have to answer.

The Hatzalah ambulance arrived, and the medic gave Motty a painful injection. A couple of minutes later, a Magen David Adom ambulance, its siren blaring, turned the corner. They also gave him a shot.

When Motty arrived at the hospital, he was unconscious and having a hard time breathing. Only after proper treatment was he finally released, *baruch Hashem*.

*   *   *

A few days later, Motty returned to the classroom, healthy as ever. The teacher asked him to say a few words. Motty thanked everyone for caring about him and writing him letters. He gave special thanks to Yossi for telling the teacher, which saved him. Then Motty said that he'd talked things over with his parents and he had some important things to tell us.

"I played a prank by bringing in the snuffbox, and it almost cost me my life. Sometimes, there are things

that kids are excited about doing, but if they thought about it a little, they wouldn't do it. If I'd thought about it a little beforehand, I would have realized that putting chemical stuff like that into my body wasn't healthy. My father told me he'd thought it was so obvious that he'd never thought to warn me. It never occurred to him that I would take his snuffbox.

"Also, it was wrong to take something that didn't belong to me.

"And one more thing, maybe the most important thing of all."

And then Motty told us the story of Peter, the shepherd boy who ran into his village crying, "Wolf!" Everyone thought that a wolf was attacking his sheep and rushed out with sticks and axes to chase away the wolf. But when they got there, Peter just laughed at them.

"Why did you cry wolf?" they asked him.

"I didn't say one came. I just shouted 'wolf.' What's wrong with that?"

Peter did it a second time, too.

Then one day a wolf came and attacked his flock of sheep. Peter raced to the village and cried out, "Wolf!" But everyone just laughed at him and said, "You're not going to fool us a third time."

The wolf devoured half of Peter's flock, which was

a big loss for him. People told him later, "That's what happens when you fool people and play pranks on them. In the end, even when you tell the truth, people don't believe you."

"During those moments," Motty told us, "when I felt like I was about to faint, I felt like I couldn't breathe, and I didn't even have the strength to say it. I pushed myself, though, and I did say it. I knew I needed help. But Yossi started to laugh. When I saw he didn't believe me, I knew that none of you would believe me. I thought I'd probably just die right here in the classroom with everyone watching, and only after I died would everyone realize that this time it was for real. They'd even be mad at me for tricking them all those years and making them not believe me.

"That's what was going through my mind right then. I was positive I was going to lose my life, and I felt bad that I'd brought it on myself. The miracle was that Yossi finally believed me even though so many times in the past I'd just been faking. I want to thank Yossi again for believing me this time, despite everything.

"I hereby declare to everyone that from now on, I won't pretend to faint or fall. So if you see me fall, know it's for real. I'm never going to play stupid tricks like that again, and I think all of you should act the same way."

I'm passing on to you what Motty said. Any substance that you're not supposed to drink or smell can be dangerous, so the best thing is not to use it, even if it makes you feel good. I suggest you stay far away from glue or any other substance you might be curious about. It's poison. It's life-threatening. If you think it might be fun to try a substance like that, remember this story. Remember that death is staring you in the face.

And it's no less important to remember the shepherd's punishment. Don't lose your friends by doing things that will make them not believe you.

That's the story, and I think that if it saves even one person's life, it was worth sharing.

"...According to His Nature"

My name is Yehudah.

I'm fourteen and a half, and I live in Yerushalayim.

There are fourteen children in our family, and I'm the oldest. My father works in education, and my mother as a medical secretary. Our home in considered a good, strong home, and we attended the best schools in the city.

My parents always valued me and treated me with the respect due the eldest child in the family. My father enjoyed talking to me and sharing all sorts of things with me that were going on in the world. When I was younger, he was very proud of me and used to brag about me and all the clever things I said.

A couple of years ago, all that changed. I'm talking about the problems that started between my parents and me. I don't remember exactly how it all began, but

I think it started when I asked them for something they didn't want to give me and then I was so fresh that it shocked them. My father tried talking to me and explained to me that my behavior was out of bounds. But I kept on being *chutzpadik*, and things got even more complicated.

From then on, my life took a downward turn. I did all I could to embitter my parents' lives. My parents tried all sorts of approaches with me—sometimes reward, sometimes punishment, guided, of course, by experts or sometimes even on their own.

I was smart enough to listen and understand what those experts must have said about me. They all said there was a big gap between my intelligence and my emotions. In intelligence, I was like someone thirty years old, while emotionally, I was three. I dismissed this assessment as if I were a thirty-year-old and was angry at it like a three-year-old.

I was a stubborn, argumentative boy. Though my parents gave me everything I asked for, I felt like the most miserable kid in the world. I felt like I deserved a lot of pity because even my own parents were against me. What could be worse than that?

My parents sent me to all sorts of counselors, yet the problems didn't end but only got worse. I saw that attending school was very important to my parents, so I used that to squeeze all sorts of things out of them. They had to give me anything I wanted, "or else I won't go to school." As time went on, though, things reached a point where even if they gave me what I wanted, I still didn't go to school. All their attempts to punish me were greeted by my going on a rampage. I'd annoy my brothers and sisters and impose a reign of terror on the whole house.

Deep inside, I knew I wasn't acting right. There were even times when I went to my parents sobbing and saying I admitted that the way I was behaving was wrong and promising to change. But I soon reverted to my old behavior.

I look back on those days and don't understand how my parents survived. I don't know how many people would have managed to hold their ground with a child who put them down, threatened them, mocked them, and was *chutzpadik* to them — and in front of their other children no less.

* * *

One day two years ago, a teacher asked me to learn with a young yeshivah student in our neighborhood. His name was Micha. I refused at first, but because this

teacher spoke nicely and it was an accepted thing to do in our school, I agreed.

I liked Micha from the minute I met him. He had an interesting way of learning with me, and each time he'd tell me an entertaining story from his life and talk about what was going on in the world. I think he reminded me of the good times I used to have with my father. But what drew me to him the most was his sense of humor. He was a really funny person. Not funny like when it's a joke (though he did tell good jokes) but funny with words. He used all kinds of funny words and expressions he made up himself. He knew how to describe something that happened in his yeshivah in such a humorous way that I'd burst out laughing right along with him.

He admired me and used to tell me so all the time. He told me he'd never met a boy as smart as I was, as well-behaved, as tactful. I squirmed when I heard him say that. On the one hand, I enjoyed it. But on the other, I said to myself, *If he only knew…*

One Shabbos, he invited me to his yeshivah. He introduced me to a few friends of his, and we ate the Shabbos *seudah* together with them and sang. I felt comfortable around them, as if I was their age, but I knew it didn't mean all that much. I'd always gotten along with people older than me (except for my parents).

I began to admire Micha. Deep inside, I decided I wanted to be just like him, someone who learned and was also a *chevrehman* with plenty of friends, someone who knew just about the whole world.

I wanted to tell him everything that was happening to me at home, but I didn't. Maybe it was because I didn't want him to know I had problems, and maybe because I knew he thought so highly of me. I'd feel ashamed for him to find out about my other side, the side he didn't know about.

But one day, it happened.

During one of those huge explosions of shouting and hitting that I created in the house, I ran away from home.

I wandered the streets in my slippers. It was one in the morning, and I didn't know what to do with myself. Being out there on the streets like that was just about the worst thing in the world, especially for a spoiled kid like me. But going home would be humiliating.

The last time I'd done it, my parents came out looking for me and begged me to come home, and I acted like I was doing them a big favor. This time, though, they didn't come looking for me, which made me even madder.

What do they think, that they'll teach me a lesson? I'll teach them a lesson!

I was thinking of what I'd do to teach them a lesson but decided against it because I really did want to go home. I knew I was just bringing suffering on myself. As I was going back and forth in my mind, I suddenly saw Micha coming toward me.

Before I could turn around and disappear, he said very casually, "Good evening, Yuda. What are you doing here at this time of night?"

"Uh...nothing. Taking a walk," I said.

"Wearing slippers?" he said without missing a beat. "Nice try. You're in trouble, right?"

He didn't leave me much choice. "More or less," I admitted

"So you're coming with me, more or less, to my yeshivah right now," he said to me. "I would tell you to go home, but I have a feeling that if you're here at this time of night and not home, that's a good reason to suggest you come to my yeshivah."

I grinned sheepishly. He understood everything. There was no point in denying what he'd said.

We arrived at the yeshivah, and there he asked me to call my parents to let them know I was with him. I had no problem with doing that. He took me to the dining room and got me a full meal (as if it was sup-pertime and not one in the morning). After that, he sat me down and said, "You don't owe me a thing, but I think you might want to tell me what's going on."

Somehow, it came out. I told him everything that was going on between my parents and me. He listened without saying anything. He didn't try to defend my parents, but he also didn't say I was right. He just sat there listening intently, and when I finished, he said, "What you're saying is very interesting, but I can't tell you why."

That caught my interest.

"Because…?" I tried.

"Nope. Not a chance," he said. But then he softened and said, "I'll think about it, but not today."

He suggested I go home. I agreed. He accompa-nied me. My parents greeted me without asking any questions.

*   *   *

A week went by before Micha and I got together again and could talk freely. I was expecting him to tell me what had been so interesting about my story, but he didn't do that, and I preferred not to ask.

He talked with me about kids who don't get along

that well with their parents. He told me that a lot of them are either the oldest child in the family or stupid kids or smart kids, and he also explained to me, in a very humorous manner, why these kids acted as they did. It was as if he was on the side of the stupid ones, but they came out looking even more stupid than they actually were.

And then I asked him, "Why are you blaming the kids? Where are the parents in the picture?"

He looked at me, sighed deeply, and asked, "Tell me something. Do your parents ever hit you hard?"

"No," I said. "They don't hit me at all."

"Do they hurt your feelings by humiliating you? Do they mock you? Laugh at you? Do they speak badly about you to the other children? Not allow you to open your mouth?"

"Not exactly," I said. "But they're full of anger toward me. They're angry all the time."

He listened and didn't comment.

"Tell me, do they withhold food from you, clothing, games, trips, and things you enjoy?"

"No," I said. "I've got plenty."

He looked at me and didn't say a thing. I felt I was right and very unfortunate and that everyone was against me.

And then he said to me, "I know exactly how you feel."

It was like he was inside my heart. He started to tell me what I was feeling, about my anger and my situation at home, about my confrontations with my parents, and what I wanted to happen and what actually took place, and how angry I was with my parents and how much I loved them, and how frustrated I was and how I didn't know what to do with myself. He said I was an open book.

I discovered I enjoyed listening to him.

"How do you know all this?" I asked.

"Because I was just like you," he said.

His secret was out.

* * *

He began telling me about his childhood. It turns out his parents were a lot like mine. Not exactly, though. They were stricter, and they also hit him sometimes, but he described himself as being a pretty insufferable child.

He told me things he did to his parents, like running away a couple of times and embarrassing them. A few times he did things that made him get kicked out of school and get into trouble with other kids. I listened to him and couldn't believe he was talking about Micha, the amazing, smart Micha standing there in front of me. He described to me someone who terrorized the neighborhood and terrorized his family. He said if there'd been a contest between the two of us for "worst kid in the world," he would have beat me hands down, without even trying.

When he finished, I asked him, "How did you become the person you are today?"

"How I got here is a story of its own."

He didn't tell me that same day. We agreed to continue the conversation. In the meantime, things between my parents and I settled down. And this conversation cemented the relationship between Micha and me.

About a month later, he told me what changed him.

"They got me a tutor," he said, "someone who came to talk with me about myself and about my life. Somehow he managed to understand all my problems at home and with myself, at school and with myself, and in the neighborhood and with myself."

We both laughed.

"You sure sound problematic."

"He built me, that tutor," he said.

"That's actually what you're doing for me, isn't it?"

"No. I'm just learning Gemara with you. You're the one who's pestering me to talk," he said with a smile.

In the following months, he told me a lot about himself and about his relationship with his parents.

Those conversations were fascinating because he showed me both sides. He was open about his perspectives as a child (the point of view I identified with), but on the other hand, he described how much his parents suffered because of him. Each time I heard a different story, but the bottom line was obvious: nothing justified my behavior.

"So, how do you explain it?" I asked. "Why did you really do it to them?"

"Because I had a difficult adolescence," he explained. "Adolescence is not an easy time. Children stop being children and slowly become youths. A child who becomes a youth feels like he's smarter than anyone, and his emotions and body go through all sorts of changes he doesn't always know how to control."

I felt like he was talking about me.

"So how did that tutor help you?"

"He listened to me in a nonjudgmental way. He didn't try to tell me that I was wrong. Mostly he asked questions whose answers made me understand things. What changed me was that he helped me mature by showing me both sides of things. He caused the child in me to grow up and managed to connect my intelligence to my emotions. Within just a few years, I'd become a clear-thinking, balanced youth. I made up with my parents and began bringing them *nachas* instead of the suffering I'd caused them in my younger years."

When he said that, tears filled my eyes. I knew that was exactly what I was doing to my parents—causing them suffering, and plenty of it.

"I'd like to meet your tutor," I said to him.

"Sure!" he said. "I'll ask if it's okay with him. He's a very special person and very wise, and I'm sure that if the two of you hit it off, it can only be good."

* * *

From then on, things got a lot better. There were fewer fights at home, and my behavior became more mature. My teachers started saying things about me I'd never heard before—praise and amazement at the change in me. My parents were excited about the miracle taking place before their eyes and expressed that both verbally and with the presents they showered upon me.

At long last, when I came home, I felt like I was

coming to a place where the people who lived there weren't afraid of me, where my siblings weren't scared I'd hit them or hurt them. My relationship with my parents changed so dramatically as to be unrecognizable. You could say I grew up.

I was accepted into a leading yeshivah, and I'll start learning there next year. But it's not in Yerushalayim. I'm very happy about the move, but there's one thing that's hard: leaving Micha. We've become very close, and I know I owe him.

We agreed that this won't be a separation. We'll keep in touch, even though we'll have to give up our regular learning sessions and our daily talks.

* * *

On Shavuos, we stayed up all night learning. Before Shacharis, I said to him, "You know, you owe me something."

"Remind me," he said.

"You promised to introduce me to your tutor. You said he was a very special person. I waited patiently and didn't pressure you. I think the time has come."

"No problem," he said. "Let's go meet him. We'll look for him together. I think he learns in a shul nearby. Let's go there."

I was curious. I wanted to meet the man who had succeeded in making the change in Micha, the special *bachur* who was my teacher for life.

As we walked, we talked about my plans and his plans, and he gave me a few basic tips for how to succeed in yeshivah. After twenty minutes, we arrived at a shul I knew very well.

He led me to a side room and said, "I'll bring him here, and you can talk."

I waited tensely.

The door opened.

Micha entered first.

And after him…

After him, my father walked in.

* * *

Shock! I remember exactly what went through my mind at that moment.

My first thought was, *What's my father doing here?*

The second was, *How can I explain to him about the third person who will be coming in?*

And then I got it.

"Let me introduce you," Micha said. "This is my tutor, the special man I told you about, the one you wanted to meet so much. It's your father. I'm happy I succeeded in returning to him what he gave me."

My father and I gave each other a big hug and cried on each other's shoulders. Millions of thoughts flashed through my mind. When we ended, we discovered we were alone. Micha was smart enough to leave us alone at that special moment.

I realized that everything that took place was planned by my father. He hadn't been able to reach me or become close to me, but he'd found a way to send an angel who would give me what he wanted to give me but that I didn't want to receive from him. Suddenly many things became clear to me, like how that first meeting took place, that night when Micha had left his yeshivah to meet me "by chance"—when it was actually at my father's request. I understood a lot of other things, and they're much longer than this story.

*   *   *

My story teaches that even a big educational expert, an *ish chinuch* like my father, might not always get along with all of his children. It's not necessarily his fault. And it doesn't always have to be anyone's fault, either.

In my case, my story was one of the most difficult for a parent to handle.

In the end, my father, my teacher, whom I love and admire, is the person who made the difference in my life. If not directly, then through a boy he had saved. And this is the time to thank Hashem for sending me people who made me what I am today—my tutor and my tutor's tutor: my father.

My father, my teacher.

Alone Against the Current

My name is Hodaya.

I'm twenty, and I live in Petach Tikvah.

Though I'm no longer a child, my story belongs in *Kids Speak*.

I've been volunteering for a few years in an organization called Notnim Koach [Giving Strength]. You know this organization well thanks to Racheli, your wonderful, special daughter.

Over the past two years, the organization opened a center for kids with autism. It's supported by the Welfare Department and operates every afternoon, staffed by amazing volunteers. I have the privilege of being in charge of the center three days a week. My job is to make sure everything is running smoothly.

On Wednesday 28 Tammuz 5779 / July 31, 2019, as a special treat, we took all fifty of the center's volunteers on a trip. We went way up north, and that's where our story begins.

We climbed into kayaks, six girls to a kayak, full of energy, shouting as loudly as we could. In the middle of the route, we all stopped—naturally without the permission of the operators—and started having water fights and splashing each other.

The youngest volunteer, seeing me, her supervisor, in a playful mood, threw me into the water, and everyone went wild.

I climbed back into our kayak and we continued the route, trying to stay close to our best friends and not lose eye contact with the other kayaks.

Our kayak had only five girls in it: me, my sister Tehillah who's in twelfth grade, my sister Moriah who's going into ninth grade, and another two girls: Noa and Shira.

The kayak with our best friends got stuck while ours continued downstream. We reached a place where there was sort of an island made of rocks. We decided that two girls would leap out of the kayak and pull it up onto the edge of the island. We'd wait there for our friends to catch up with us so that we could all continue on together.

I was the first one out. As soon as my feet touched

the water near the island, I could feel the current was moving very fast. By the time I realized what that meant, it was too late. The kayak was pulled downstream before I could grab hold of it to pull it up onto the island. I tried to swim after it, but it moved faster than I could swim. Though the current swept me toward it, I couldn't get close enough to grab it.

When the kayak reached a shallow area, my sister Tehillah jumped into the water to help me. She managed to hold herself steady against the rushing water, but I struggled, still trying to reach the kayak with no success. Meanwhile, the water was rising higher and higher until finally, that was it. Suddenly, I was going under. All I could hear was the roar of water rushing past me. I tried to lift my head above the water, but I couldn't. I tried to swim, but the current was stronger than I was. At those moments, all I could think of was, *Hashem! I don't want to die!*

I was sure my life was over.

Inside, I was crying and pleading, *Hashem, please get me out of here. You're the only One Who can save me.*

I tried to kick with my feet, but it didn't help. The current was just too strong. I felt my feet getting tangled in something. As I struggled to free them, I was pulled further downstream by the current.

In my heart, I kept screaming to Hashem to save me because there was no way I could save myself. Everyone else had been swept downstream in the kayak by the strong current. I couldn't hear a thing except for the crazy roar of rushing water. And then, after what seemed like an eternity, I felt powerful hands grab me under my shoulders and lift me out of the water. I discovered myself standing stunned on a submerged boulder in the stream, facing my sister Tehillah who was shivering with cold and shock.

We stood there hugging each other, trembling and crying like two little kids.

Around us were groups of girls still in their kayaks, but because of the wild current, none of them were able to stop. Then two more kayaks passed by. The second one managed to stop and beach itself on solid ground. In it sat Esther, a close friend who's almost like a sister to me (which deserves a story of its own). She had seen us and, with superhuman effort, managed to stop her kayak. She climbed out to get as close to us as she could.

We didn't dare move an inch from where we stood because the water around us was deep. We were scared to death to let go of each other for even a second.

Two other kayaks passed by, and our friends

shouted out to everyone to call someone or to stop next to us, but due to the powerful current, not a single one was able to.

* * *

After about twenty minutes, a kayak came with a kayak company employee, but he also couldn't stop near us. He did manage to stop on the opposite bank, though. From there, he told us how to get onto solid ground to make our way to the kayak of Esther and her friends. All this time, Esther was standing on land as close as possible to us, giving us support just by being there for us.

We climbed up as directed, trying to avoid the thorn bushes and rocks, the bugs and creepy-crawlies. The main thing was that finally, we were standing on solid ground, all in one piece.

After getting into Esther's kayak, we were carried downstream. On the way, we met friends who'd taken Noa with them. She was so terrified that when she saw us, she started crying again.

We sang *"Tov L'Hodot LaHashem"* together (it's recommended that people who go through a traumatic experience should sing).

We got to the shore where more friends who were

worried about us were waiting, but now we focused on one concern: what had happened to Moriah and Shira, who'd remained alone in our original kayak? We quickly boarded our bus, which drove us to our starting point.

I cried the whole way there. I don't even want to tell you what thoughts were running through my mind. I thought about Moriah and Shira and felt that I wouldn't be able to cope with whatever news I was surely going to hear.

We reached the bus, crying and trembling, and there…

We found everyone safe and sound! Shira's hand was bandaged due to a branch that had scratched her, but that was it.

Thank You, Hashem!

* * *

After we'd relaxed and caught our breath, I asked Noa what had happened during those moments when I was under the water, and she told me something that amazed me. She said that as soon as the water covered me, I began to struggle. My sister was crying and shouting, "Help!" But then she tried to swim against the current to get to me.

Noa described how hard it was, and in two sentences, summed up everything: "I don't understand how Tehillah managed to fight the current and reach you. It must have been sister power."

And that's what calmed me down, knowing that I had a sister there for me and that thanks to her, I'm here, thanks to the love that exists between sisters. Thanks to this power called "sisters," I'm alive and well today.

Powerful emotions filled me.

In the water, I felt that everything I'd ever done, that all the people I'd ever known—nothing could have helped me then. Only Hashem could help me. I was submerged in the fast-moving current, unable to do anything except to keep playing in my mind the shout for help that only Hashem could hear. I was sure there was nothing anyone could do to get me out, but He heard me and helped me.

Then all my amazing friends, younger than me by two and three years, encouraged me and hugged me and expressed such love that you can't find anywhere.

*   *   *

At night, after returning home and telling my mother about everything that happened, Tehillah and I cried again like two little kids. After that, I sat and thought about everything I'd done in my twenty years of life. In what merit did Hashem choose to leave me alive? Why did I get to stay here on earth with my family? What possible merits could I, a plain, ordinary girl, have?

Since then, no matter what's happening, I say thank you to Hashem for the privilege of being here, safe and sound, walking around my house, hugging my little brothers, talking to my grandparents, davening in the morning. Everything.

* * *

I wrote this story so you could warn people to obey all the rules and regulations of a site when they travel. These instructions aren't posted just for decoration. Their purpose is to prevent incidents like the one I just told you about.

Be especially careful if you go kayaking. Since our story took place, I've heard about a lot of instances of people falling in the water because they went where they weren't supposed to. I don't understand why they let people take kayaks down dangerous rapids without a professional guide assigned to accompany each group.

Baruch Hashem, I am here to give a warning. Hashem

could have taken me to Him, but He left me here, and this is what I have to say now:

"Be careful, everyone! All the rules and regulations are there to protect you. Even if you know how to swim or can jump from a height, be *careful*! Remember what it says: 'Be very careful to safeguard your lives' (*Devarim* 4:15)."

Making Friends with Anxiety

My name is Shmulik.

I'm thirteen, and I live in Yerushalayim.

My family and friends will tell you I'm a funny kid. They say that because if you talk to me for more than five minutes, chances are I'm going to tell a joke or say something clever that will make you laugh or at least smile.

Everyone is sure that I'm a boy who's always laughing, always relaxed and happy. But it's not true.

You probably won't believe me, but ever since I can remember, I've been afraid of lots of things. When we go on a trip, I'm afraid we'll get lost and not be able to find our way back. When my parents leave the house, I'm afraid something bad will happen to them. Sometimes before a long trip I even imagine us running out of gas and getting stuck in the middle of the desert.

You're probably saying to yourself right now, "Wow, what a bad joke, a funny kid who's always scared." Okay, so it's a little more complicated than that because no one knows I'm afraid. In school, for instance, I feel safe, and when the whole family is home, there's not too much to worry about, either.

Usually, it only happens when I go on a trip or when my parents go to a wedding. After half an hour or so I start imagining all kinds of bad things that can happen, and then I quickly call my father's cell phone and check to see that they're okay.

The call sounds something like this:

"Hello?"

"Hi, Shmulik. Is everything okay?"

"Where are you?"

"We're at the wedding. The chuppah just ended."

"When will you be home?"

"In about two hours."

"Okay, Abba. See you."

After I talk to my parents, I feel calmer. But then, half an hour later, I wonder if something might have happened. Sometimes when I hear an ambulance siren, my brain immediately connects it to my parents, and so I call them again.

"Hello?"

"Yes, Shmulik."

"Ima, where are you?"

"We're still at the wedding."

"Wow, how long are you going to stay?"

"Shmulik, sweetie, why aren't you sleeping now?"

"I'm not tired..." (That's not entirely true. The correct answer is that I'm worried about them and want them to come home already.)

"Shmulik, everything's okay. We'll probably be back very late, so go to sleep."

"Okay, Ima."

"Good night, Shmulik."

I'm usually calm for about half an hour after this type of conversation. I go take a snack or read something and then I call again.

*   *   *

You probably realize that eventually, my parents get a little mad at me. Though they never say it, I hear it in their voices.

Once, my father took me for a "private talk." That's a talk he has with each of us kids every now and then. We'd sit together in a room, alone, just him and me. He told me that I was a big boy and that it wasn't appropriate for me to act like this.

"Your mother and I can't be on the phone with you all the time," he said. "It's very disturbing,"

"But when you're not here, I worry about you a lot," I explained. "I'm afraid something will happen to you and Ima."

"Nonsense," my father said with a smile. "You know Hashem watches over us continually. Don't we say "Hamalach Hagoel" every night before going to sleep? You've just got to believe in it strongly!"

"But all sorts of bad things happen all the time," I said quietly.

"True, but Hashem is still protecting us," my father said, trying to encourage me to be strong. "Don't worry, Shmulik!"

"Okay, Abba," I said.

But I didn't know how to stop.

*　*　*

When I was in fourth grade, we took our annual school trip. Like the rest of my friends, I excitedly filled a backpack with candy and snacks and planned who I'd sit next to and who I'd hike with. I had a great time on the bus ride. We sang songs and laughed a lot, and the teacher told us riddles. I was in a great mood.

And then we got to the hiking trail. It was in a

desert-like area with lots of sand and boulders. Above us, the sun was blazing. Our guide started marching forward, followed by my classmates and me. We walked and walked, but the trail just didn't end. Even at the horizon, the path extended on and on. I could see only bare hills with no people or roads where cars could reach.

I heard the guide say there was at least an hour before sunset.

And then...I began to imagine.

I imagined that we wouldn't be able to find the trail and we'd be lost in the desert. In my mind, I pictured dozens of people looking for us and not finding us.

I tried to drink a lot so as not to dehydrate. I kept looking ahead to see if we were nearing the end, but after every hill we climbed, we saw another one. I was terrified.

"Shmulik, are you okay?" Bentzi asked me. "You seem so weak all of a sudden."

"Uh, I'm fine," I replied with a smile. "When is this hike ever going to end?"

"Everyone stop right here," I heard the guide say. "These hills are full of streams that are usually dry at this time of year but are flooded right now. We won't be able to cross where I thought we would."

"What?!" I heard myself cry out. "Then…then what are we going to do?"

The guide looked at me and then said, "We're going to turn around and go back the way we came."

"The whole way?" I asked fearfully.

"Yes," the guide said and smiled.

Now my imagination really started to go wild. Here's the picture: one confused guide and a bunch of kids standing in front of a churning stream, not knowing which way to go. The sun is blazing down on them, their water is running out, and there's no cell phone reception, so there's no way to call the police or rescue teams.

"Shmulik, are you all right?"

This time his voice sounded far away, and then suddenly I felt dizzy and collapsed on the ground.

*   *   *

"He must be dehydrated!" I heard someone say. "Lift him up."

I felt someone washing my face and lifting me onto his shoulders. That was the guide.

"Shmulik, wake up," he said to me in a cheerful voice. "We're almost back at the beginning of the path."

I wasn't dehydrated. I think I just panicked and

collapsed. We got back to the bus, where I recovered completely. I even joked with my friends who were looking at me half concerned and half confused.

"What happened? What's the matter? Why did you panic?" the guide asked me. "What did you think would happen?"

I didn't say anything.

For a long time afterward, I refused to go on any trips. Each time I came up with a different excuse for why I wasn't going. My friends tried to persuade me to come, but I was afraid the same thing that happened on that trip would happen to me to again, so I preferred to have a free day at home with my mother.

All this time, I continued to bother my parents with phone calls when they were out, calling them about every half an hour to ask when they were coming home. Sometimes they didn't answer the call, and then I would cry and get angry. They had no idea what to do.

One day, my father took me aside and said, "Shmulik, I want you to talk to someone about your fears."

"Who?"

"A young man named Eli," my father said. "He's a friend of mine, and he understands children's fears."

I didn't say anything.

"So, what do you say?" he asked. "It will be in my office. Talk to him a little. Maybe it will help you."

Deep inside, I knew I had no good reason to refuse it, but still, I asked, "Is he some kind of psychologist?"

My father laughed. "You're a smart kid. Yes, he's...a kind of psychologist."

"Okay," I said, "but don't tell anyone. I don't want people to think I'm a kid with problems."

"Fine," my father promised me. "And Shmulik... you may be a kid with a problem, but you're also a very smart, talented boy who just needs to learn to handle his emotions."

*   *   *

I felt a little nervous as I walked into my father's office, but I was very curious to know what this person was going to say. Inside the office a young man with a smile was waiting for me. My father said he had some errands to take care of and would be back in about half an hour.

I nodded my okay.

"I'm Eli," said the man as he placed a small binder on the table.

"Shmulik," I replied.

"I understood from your father that you're very

afraid when your parents leave the house," he said. "Tell me a little bit about it."

I told him. He listened very carefully, and then he asked me a strange question: "Shmulik, do you know what a graph is?"

"A graph?" I wrinkled my forehead. "No."

Eli pulled a page out of his binder. He drew a vertical line on the left side of the page, and above it wrote: "Fear 10." In the middle he wrote, "Fear 5," and at the bottom he wrote, "Calm."

"This is your ladder of fear," he explained. "Your line starts from the left at the minute your parents leave the house. I want you to try drawing me a graph of your fear beginning with that moment. When you feel that you stop being calm and start to feel the fear, the line rises. I want to know how scared you are."

I thought a little and then took the pen and drew a slow rise to the highest level of fear, and I wrote the word "phone," and from there I drew the line right down to the word "calm." Then the line went up again to "phone," and then down again to "calm."

"When I call my parents," I explained to him, "at that moment, I completely stop being afraid because I know they're okay. But then, after a while I start worrying about them again until the next phone call, and so on."

Eli looked at my graph in admiration and said, "You're a very smart boy, do you know that? I thought it would take me a long time to explain this process, but you already understood it by yourself. The phone calls don't really calm you down. They just make it so that you don't have to deal with the anxiety at that moment."

I glowed from the compliment he'd just given me. I felt that he understood me and knew what I was going through.

We continued to talk a little more about this process of anxiety, and then my father returned and took me home.

Before saying a friendly goodbye to Eli, I arranged to meet with him the following week.

* * *

When we met again, Eli explained to me that when I'm anxious, my body automatically enters a state of high alert. It becomes flooded with a substance called adrenaline, which causes rapid breathing and a desire to escape or run somewhere. He taught me that everything begins with my thoughts and continues with my body's response to a false sense of danger.

"You're a child with a lot of imagination," he said,

"and that will never change. What you can do, though, is learn to control your thoughts. It takes practice, but it can be done."

We talked about the remote possibility of something bad happening to my parents or me, and about the ways I can help my body get unstressed—by relaxation, slow breathing, or just by distracting it by playing or another activity.

We agreed that the next time my parents left the house, I would wait a full hour before calling them, and after that, another full hour. "That way," he explained, "we'll keep the phone calls apart on that graph, and slowly but surely you'll see that the line marking your level of anxiety will go down, too, because you will learn to become friends with it."

* * *

We worked on it for a few months. Slowly but surely, I felt more in control of my anxiety using the methods Eli taught me, and then our meetings ended, and Eli disappeared from my life.

I was proud of myself.

In the sixth grade, I agreed for the first time in about two years to go on the annual trip. I was very scared, but as the day went by and I had fun with my friends, I forgot about my fears and convinced myself that the same way everyone else wasn't scared, I didn't need to be either.

I enjoyed that trip more than any other in my life because I was able to make friends with my anxiety.

*   *   *

At my bar mitzvah, I suddenly saw Eli coming to join us. He stayed for a few minutes, shook my hand and my father's hand, and then left, after giving me a gift-wrapped present.

It was a small book titled *Emunah v'Bitachon*, by the Chazon Ish. Inside, he'd written:

> *"Dear Shmulik! I'm very proud of you for what you've accomplished. You've proven that you can control your thoughts and feelings and not let them control you. You are now bar mitzvah, and a mature teenager with all that means. I hope you will always remember that there is Someone Above Who is protecting you and that you will never be afraid again, for Hashem is always at your side."*

Since that night, I've never seen Eli again, but I'll always remember the changes I made with his help.

To kids everywhere, I want to say, you can learn

something from my story. You can make friends with your anxiety and not let it take over or prevent you from doing happy things and good things.

And if not, at least you've learned what a graph is.

Absolute Trust

My name is Uri.

I'm twelve years old, and I live in Tel Aviv.

I'm a very friendly, popular kid. Until a year ago, I went to a regular school, but at the end of the year I transferred to a different school.

The reason I changed schools is simple: the last year I learned there (in fifth grade), I was hardly ever at school.

Do you want to know why?

There are a lot of reasons, but none of them is the real reason. You could chalk it up to fatigue, learning difficulties, social problems, my parents' bad relationship with me, my siblings talking back to me.

Any more excuses?

Let's not waste time with this because none of them are true. I have no difficulty learning. Just the opposite. Whenever I put my mind to it, I was at the top of my class.

I certainly didn't have social problems. I've always had lots of friends. As for my parents, they didn't have a bad relationship with *me*; I had a bad relationship with *them*. I acted fresh to them and didn't do what they asked.

The reason I didn't go to school was that I just didn't feel like it. And at the end of the year, my school didn't feel like keeping me there, so I found myself at another school.

You know without me telling you that the second school wasn't a better school than the first. The opposite. But just in case you don't know why, I'll explain.

There are various levels of schools. There are high-level schools, regular schools, and schools on a lower level.

Children who do not succeed in the high-level schools are forced to go to a regular-level school, and those who don't succeed there, have to go to a lower-level school—because no high-level school is anxious to take in a kid who failed at a different school.

Since the school I attended in fifth grade was a regular-level school, the only school that would agree to accept me was a school for special ed.

I have no problem with special ed schools, but they're for children who need special education, and I don't. I could get good grades, I just hadn't tried. At the special ed school I saw that I already knew everything they were learning, so I didn't feel like I was in the right place.

What do you think happened?

Exactly. I decided not to go.

I stayed home and slept till late in the afternoon, after which I'd get up and start pestering everyone.

When my parents tried to stop me, I'd talk back to them and do some very not nice things that I'm ashamed to tell you.

Eventually, my daily routine became unbearable to them. The fact that they couldn't wake me up in the morning, that I slept late into the afternoon…and then the constant quarrels with my siblings, which stemmed from boredom and frustration.

It seemed like nothing could change the situation. I have five brothers and sisters, and they all go to school. Everyone works hard, has lots of friends, is happy with their life. I'm the only one who's lonely, full of anger, and bothers everyone until they can't stand me, and I can't stand them.

One day my parents came into my room quietly and asked to speak to me. This kind of thing happened about once a week, so I didn't get excited.

They brought me a letter, and this is what it said:

Dear Uri,

After consulting with a number of educational experts, we've decided to inform you, out of love and caring, that the current situation can no longer go on in this way and that we will not continue to allow certain of your behaviors and habits.

From now on, we intend to do whatever it takes to change the situation. Therefore, we have decided to inform you that:

1. We will not accept talking back or any controlling behavior, and certainly no violence, from you. Every instance of such behavior will be dealt with in all severity.

2. You must go to school. You will no longer be allowed to stay home during school hours.

3. We do not forget for a minute all your good qualities—your gentle nature, your common sense, your seriousness, and your many talents. Our intention, with determination and caring, is to remove the obstacles in your way that prevent you from being a good, loyal, wonderful son.

Love,

Abba and Ima

* * *

I read the letter. It was really weird. I had never received a letter in my life, and certainly not such a harsh letter from my parents. At first, I didn't know what to do, but when I reread the letter, it really made me mad.

What do you think I did?

I tore it to shreds.

My parents didn't react. All they said was, "We were expecting you to do that, so we made a few copies. Actually, the letter isn't only for you, but for us. We've decided to save you at any cost, and we gave you a copy, so you'd know what we plan to do." They left the room.

And I said to myself, *Let's see them try.*

* * *

In the morning, my father came to my room and said, "You need to leave the house."

I opened one eye and said, "I'm tired."

"I realize that you're tired," my father said, "but according to our decision, you need to be out of the house during school hours."

"I'm tired, and I don't feel like it," I said with chutzpah.

"We respect you, so we'll give you five minutes to get dressed," my father said. "You don't have to go

to school. You just need to be out of the house during school hours. You must obey our decision. If you're not dressed in five minutes, I'll take you outside the front door and leave you there, even if you're in your pajamas."

My father left, and I started getting dressed. I put on my pants, but then I said to myself, *Wait a minute. I'm tired. So why should I do this?* I went back into bed.

My father came back into the room. "I see you're partially dressed. Do you want to put on a shirt?"

"No."

"Then I'll have to take you out in your pajamas," my father said.

"No."

At this point, my father lifted me out of bed and took me outside the house. My mother took my shirt, socks, and shoes, and put them outside the house also.

I couldn't believe what was happening to me.

"I want to sleep!" I shouted.

"You will not enter the house until school is over for the day," my father said. "If you want, we'll let you go inside to put on your shirt."

"No! I'll stay here."

"Fine," my father said. "I'll stay with you."

We sat there for a few hours. Neighbors came

down the stairs, and one of them asked, "Why are you out here in your pajamas?" I had no answer. I mean, I did have an answer, but I didn't want the neighbors to know I didn't want to go to school. I knew they'd find it strange.

* * *

Toward one o'clock, I said to my father, "It's not right what you did to me. You can't take me out of the house in my pajamas."

"Why don't you complain about me?" my father said.

"Where should I complain?"

"Wherever you want. I'll go wherever you decide. Tell me who you want to tell that your parents are wrong for making you leave the house in your pajamas, and if they tell me I shouldn't do it, I won't."

I thought a little when suddenly I had an idea.

"You'll go with me to whoever I want?" I asked my father.

"Whoever you want," my father said.

I told him the name of a man who I'd heard protected children and fought for their rights, and who listened to them and respected them.

"Are you willing to go even to him?" I asked my father.

My father looked surprised.

"Are you willing to go to him?" I asked again.

"Yes, I'm willing to go to him," my father said.

"Great!" I said. "When should we go?"

My father said he had to make an appointment and hoped the person would agree to see us. "But until then," he added, "I stand by my word. You can't be at home during school hours."

At four, I was allowed to enter the house.

The next day, I didn't argue. I got dressed and stayed outside. The day after that, I went to school because I didn't feel like spending the day in the stairwell. It was too boring. That same day, my father notified me that the following afternoon we could go see the man I asked to go to, the one who fought for children's rights.

I knew that my misery had come to an end, because no one would let my parents put me out of the house— certainly not the person who protected the rights of children.

The next day, I went to school, and right after school let out, my parents took me to the man's office.

*   *   *

I went in. It was the first time I'd be speaking to a

professional and especially to a pretty famous person. He introduced himself and said he was trying to help children with social or family problems and trying to protect them from those who wanted to harm them. Nothing new there. I knew all that. That's why I'd come to him.

He asked my name and how old I was. I told him.

Then he asked me if something was bothering me.

"Yes, there is," I said to him. "My parents told me that they're going to put me in the stairwell in my pajamas."

He raised his eyebrows and asked, "At what time of day did they say they'd do that to you?"

"Eight-thirty in the morning."

"Wait," he said. "Isn't that when you're supposed to be in school?"

"Yes," I replied, "I'm supposed to be, but I don't feel like it."

"No child feels like going to school," he said. "It's even written even in the Gemara: 'They acted like children running away from school.' Still, all the children in the world—in China, in Saudi Arabia, in India and Japan—go to school. Because that's what they're supposed to do."

"But I'm tired, so I'm not going, so my father told

me he was going to put me outside the house in my pajamas."

"So you dressed quickly and went to school so he wouldn't do that, correct?" he said.

"Not exactly," I told him, "My father already took me out to the stairwell in my pajamas once."

The man seemed shocked. "Are you serious?"

"Totally," I said, glad I had come to the right place.

* * *

"Listen," he said to me, "there's good news and bad news. I'll start with the bad news. I'm the one who told your father to tell you he'd do that if you refused to go to school. I already told you that my job is to help children and to protect them, and a child who doesn't go to school for several months is a child in danger. Because 'bed is death.' Such a child is cut off from the world, and after a while he will not be able to connect to society, even if he wants to. So, to protect you from yourself, I told your parents that one of the most important things is regular attendance at school.

"When a child doesn't go to school for months, we must inform him that he can't stay at home during school hours. We have to specify the time when he should be out of the house, and make sure he is…even in his pajamas."

Now it was my turn to be shocked. "You're the one who gave my parents this advice?"

"Yes, it was me. As I explained to you, my job is to protect children."

I was confused. After all, I was the one who suggested to my father that we go see this man. How was it possible that my father had talked to him before I suggested it?

Then he said, "And now for the good news."

I wondered what he was going to say.

"The good news is that I have been giving this advice to parents for over twenty years, and I think hundreds of children have started going to school because of it—hundreds of children who have grown up, gotten married, and have children who go to school. But you're the first one whose father actually took him out of the house in pajamas. That never happened to me before, because all the other children got the message, got dressed, and went to school."

I didn't understand. "How come it never happened if that's what you told everyone to do?"

"Because all the children and teens who are told this say, 'Okay. I'll get up and go out.' Some might add in anger, 'I'll go out, but you should just know, I'm not going to school.' And that's fine. As long as they're not in bed. But you...well, you're the first to go out in paja-mas. That's something that's never happened before."

Then he added with a smile, "Because you're first, I should stand up for you."

I liked that for some reason.

"If you explain to me how this happened, I'll con-sider giving you a reward. I'm curious about you."

"I was tired," I told him. "I wanted to keep on sleep-ing. "

"And if there was a fire, would you still want to sleep?"

"No," I said. "If that happened, I'd get dressed fast and go out."

"So in this case, why didn't you get dressed fast and go out?"

I thought a little, and then I said, "Because I count-ed on them."

"Explain what you just said."

"My parents are weak," I said. "They can't seem to stand up to me. I counted on that—that even now, they wouldn't be able to stand up to me."

*   *   *

You have no idea how excited he was about what I said. He stood up in my honor, the way you do for important rabbis, and said to me, "Usually I teach children and tell them things they've never heard before, but now you've given me a tremendous new insight that will resonate for future generations." Then he rushed over to his bookcase and gave me a book as a gift (a book he himself wrote, which gives you a hint as to who I met with).

Then he asked me if I was ready for him to invite my parents into the room so that I could tell them exactly what I'd told him.

I said yes.

My parents entered the room, and he said to them, "Uri wants to tell you something."

I told my parents that I knew I should go to school every day and not act fresh to them, but I counted on them being weak and took advantage of it.

That began a warm, good conversation, and I felt flattered when I saw how excited he was about it.

We ended the meeting with dramatic decisions that came out of the understanding that just like I want my parents to be healthy and not sick, rich and not poor, I also want them to be strong and not weak. It's good for me.

My parents lovingly made it clear to me that I could now trust that they won't let me stay in bed, hurt my siblings, and they especially won't let me hurt myself.

That was one meeting I'll never forget.

* * *

Now we're six months after the story. I've changed for the better. I meet with the same person every week.

I want to share what I learned with other children who act the way I did (and who know even better than me that their bad behavior doesn't stem from being bad but comes from bad habits).

Today I trust my parents. No means no. And that makes me feel more secure. I listen to them and don't feel irritable all the time. I used to feel that way because my parents weren't strong enough to stand up to me.

Now that they've made it clear to me that, for my benefit, they will stand up for themselves, I feel much more secure and much happier about my life.

Leadership

My name is Nati.

I'm twelve years old, and I live in one of the Gush Etzion settlements.

I want to tell you about a boy who's a real leader. His name is Moishy, and he's in my class.

Maybe you think I'm a fan of class kings and such, but after you hear the story, I think you'll understand why it was urgent for me to write it.

In our grade, there are two parallel classes, and for some reason, over the years, a rivalry developed between the two. I don't remember how it started. It might have begun even in the first grade. Somehow, two opposing camps were created, with each one competing against the other. The healthy competition turned into rivalry and from there to actual hatred.

This created situations where kids who lived across

the street from each other suddenly started to fight, or even worse, stopped talking to each other and totally ignored one another.

The school noticed what was going on and tried hard to make things better. The principal went into each class and spoke with the kids, and the teachers did joint workshops to bring the two groups closer. The bottom line? Nothing worked. A few times, the kids themselves tried to smooth things over. They gained a few days of peace and quiet, but it didn't last. All it took was one spark for the flames of controversy and hatred to flare up. It was real *sinas chinam*. No one knew how it began or why it was still going on, but it continued in full force.

*   *   *

In the middle of last year (sixth grade), a new boy entered our class: Moishy.

As soon as he arrived, it was clear that he was unlike any boy we'd ever known.

At first, we didn't pay too much attention to him because he didn't try to stand out or make lots of friends the way some other new kids did. He seemed to be in no rush socially. The funny thing is, that's what made us all so curious about him. We began wondering who he really was, and within a few weeks, more and more kids found themselves wanting to be around him.

There was something more mature, more serious about Moishy, and yet he was always smiling and pleasant. He was an excellent student and an outstanding athlete, yet despite all his qualities, he didn't act superior or conceited.

When we found out that he was good at sports, he began to be chosen to play, and that's when we discovered another unusual aspect of his personality. Every child knows that during the game, there are always arguments about whether you touched the ball or not, or whether you touched your opponent or not. There are a lot of fights because kids find it hard to admit their mistakes, especially if it means that the ball goes to the other team.

I think no kid has ever asked himself how it happens that when one team says, "The ball hit him," every single kid in the other team will call out, "No, it didn't!" How is it possible that all ten kids on one team saw one thing and all ten kids on the other team saw another? Why wouldn't there be eight kids from one team who saw X and at least two who saw Y? Did you ever ask yourself why that never happens?

So that's just it. With Moishy, it did happen. When a kid from our team was out, even if it was Moishy himself, he'd admit it and say, "The ball hit me" or "I touched the ball with my hand." And when there were arguments about a different kind of foul, he'd say, "I didn't see it" or "I saw it, and we're disqualified." He might also say, "I saw what happened and it's not a foul."

At first, kids would get mad at him. But they got used to Moishy being fair and telling the truth even if he or his team lost out. The other boys admired him for that, and you know what? Even the opposing team trusted him when he said, "I saw it, and it's not a foul." Because, "If Moishy says it, it must be true. If he didn't see it, he wouldn't say it."

Are you beginning to understand why I said he was a leader?

* * *

Moishy has another quality that's rare.

Usually, there's no way a whole class can participate in a game. About ten boys play and the rest watch. Others might ask if they can play, too, and some don't even ask because they know they won't be chosen.

Moishy had a strange way of handling this. At some point in a game, without fail, he'd say to one of the kids that hadn't been chosen for a team, "Can you do me a favor and take my place for a few minutes?"

Naturally, the kid would agree, and we couldn't protest because Moishy decided, and that was it.

We soon realized that he was only saying he was tired, but he really wasn't. He just wanted to let the other kids play. That's another point about his leadership. He wasn't one of those who made friends only with the popular kids. He was friends with everyone, even kids who had no status—and not just during a game. Even during recess he'd go over to a boy in the schoolyard and say, "What's new? Wasn't that funny what happened in class?" In that way he made the kids no one ever paid any attention to feel great.

Now that I'm telling you all these things, I'm beginning to think that maybe there should be a whole book about Moishy titled, *How to be a Leader*. But we just got used to him, and as time went on, in the most natural way, without any fights or quarrels, he just became the class leader.

Was there an inauguration ceremony? Never. Did someone say, "Let's make Moishy our leader"? That didn't happen either. But each of us knew that Moishy was a perfect leader who did good things for everyone.

*   *   *

You'd probably like to know how things stood

between Moishy and the other class, regarding the rivalry.

It's like this. At first, he didn't seem to notice it. I guess he understood what was going on from the start, but he didn't say anything about it. And when there were fights... I don't want to describe exactly what kind of fights they were. Let me just say they included talking about people behind their backs, name-calling, verbal attacks, and even physical blows. When that happened, Moishy would just disappear from the scene. He wasn't there and didn't get involved.

I think if he'd tried to get involved right at the beginning, we would have admired him less. Moishy simply chose not to participate; if a fight started in one place, he was always somewhere else.

But one day, he couldn't sit on the sidelines. It was when the other class came into our classroom during recess and wrecked it. In response, our class went into their classroom and wrecked it too. (When I say "wrecked," I mean that backpacks and notebooks were thrown all over. Stuff like that.)

Here Moishy did get involved, and he did it in a completely natural way by saying, "We can't allow people to come into our classroom and destroy it. Let's set up guard duty."

He immediately set up shifts according to the day and time each kid was on duty to guard our classroom. He didn't ask anyone for permission, and no one said to him, "Why are you the one to decide for all of us?" I think we all felt it was the best thing to do.

What happened was that during every recess, there were attempts to break into our classroom. The guards would alert reinforcements, and all of us, including Moishy, came to help keep the door closed so the other boys couldn't come in.

Of course, this activity caused fights in which Moishy was also involved. I remember the first time the principal came into the classroom and asked who had pushed Chaim from the second class (Chaim was sort of the leader of the second class, parallel to Moishy in ours). Moishy raised his hand and said, "I take responsibility for that."

"What do you mean, you take responsibility?" the principal asked him. "Did you push him or not?"

"I don't know if I pushed Chaim specifically or someone else. I do know that I pushed."

The principal seemed both curious and amused. He was used to hearing vehement denials and seeing boys point the finger of blame at someone else. He wasn't used to a boy taking responsibility for something he wasn't even sure he did.

"Why are you taking responsibility and not someone else?"

Moishy took some time answering. "Someone needs to take responsibility, don't they?"

The whole class laughed, and the surprised look on Moishy's face told the principal he hadn't meant to be fresh. He'd just given a truthful answer. If it had been anyone else, the principal would have punished him for his chutzpah. It was clear to everyone that this was something else. What it was, we couldn't say. But we all knew it wasn't chutzpah.

"Moishy," the principal said, "if you take responsibility, you'll be punished by having to remain in the classroom during recess for the next two days.

Moishy nodded. It was not a nod of sadness or a nod of chutzpah. It was a nod of one who realizes that taking responsibility for oneself has consequences and that he was willing to pay the price.

The surprising result was that the whole class decided to stay in the classroom during recess for the next two days.

And the even more surprising result was that while we'd known for a while that Moishy was a leader, now everyone in the school knew it, too, including the staff.

*   *   *

As far as the other class was concerned, this was their signal to target Moishy.

And so, during recess, kids from the parallel class began to taunt Moishy. He didn't respond, but we rushed to his defense. He was our leader, wasn't he? Naturally, this caused fights between both sides, which led to punishment by the administration, which felt powerless to stop the fights.

We were warned by the principal that if things didn't settle down, they would break up our class and transfer students from one to the other. But when the parents heard that, they remembered how two years earlier the school had tried the same thing and it hadn't worked. Each class had ostracized the new students, and during recess, two groups formed according to the original classes and opposed each other even more forcefully. So transfering students wasn't going to be an option.

And then, just when it looked like everything had reached a dead end, the turning point came. It was so unusual and amazing that it's worth this whole story.

*   *   *

It was during recess at a time when the situation was about to explode. Hard words and threats were flying through the air when suddenly Moishy went over to Chaim. He said to him, "Let me ask you something. What do I need to do to put an end to this war?"

"What do you need to do? Just stop acting like wild little kids," Chaim answered him.

Some of the kids our side started yelling, "You're the one who's a little kid, and—"

They were silenced by Moishy holding up his hand.

"Okay, I promise in the name of my entire class, we will stop acting like wild little kids," he said. "Anything else we need to do?"

"Ask our forgiveness," Chaim said.

"If I ask your forgiveness on behalf of my whole class, then will it be finished?"

Chaim turned around in confusion to face his class. They said, "It doesn't work like that. Nothing's settled. They did a lot of damage to us and beat us up." (They sure were forgetful. No memory of what they'd done to us!)

"They're right," Moishy said, surprising everyone. "Nothing's settled. Chaim, tell me, what will settle things? Let's say you slap me across the face and punch me. Will that settle things?"

Everyone fell silent. We all looked at Moishy as if he'd landed from mars.

Moishy took advantage of the silence to say, "I don't know how this fight started. I only came here a year ago, and to this day I haven't been able to figure out what your story is. I mean, these are not the only parallel classes in the country. Every school has them. We're probably the only ones that fight each other like little kids. So, why is everyone holding grudges? Let's put an end to it. If one slap isn't enough to settle it, give me two. If one punch isn't enough, give me four—and maybe two kicks for good measure. You can choose who'll deliver this final payment. But let's put things in order and end this story."

Chaim consulted with his friends. They liked the idea of giving our leader a beating that he wouldn't give back. I don't think they considered what they would be giving up by this—stopping the ongoing fight. But it was so tempting, they couldn't resist.

After consultations, Chaim said, "Okay. We decided that two slaps will settle the matter."

"Then let's go," Moishy said. "Who did you pick?"

"Dudi," they chorused.

Dudi was the strongest boy in their class. Tall and muscular, built like an olive tree. He wasn't just the strongest kid in their class, he was the strongest boy in the whole school. And if you ask me, I don't think a single kid thought of Dudi when Moishy made his offer.

"It's a deal," we heard Moishy say. "Let it be Dudi."

All the kids in the class gathered in a circle. Believe me when I say you've never seen anything like it. The air crackled with tension. I feel it right now, as I always do whenever I remember it. Moishy, the boy who was the truest leader I've ever known, stood there fearlessly, his shoulders straight, waiting for the two slaps.

Dudi made his way to the center of the circle.

The world stood still.

Dudi raised his big hand...

Tension filled the air.

And then...

Another twist in the plot.

"I want it to be in one of the classrooms," Dudi said. "Just me and him without anyone else."

Murmurs swept through both groups. They whispered with Dudi. It turns out that he was ashamed to do it in front of everyone and preferred to settle accounts in one of the classrooms.

Everyone was a little disappointed, I must admit, but because the process had begun, they agreed.

Dudi and Moishy walked away toward one of the empty classrooms and closed themselves up in it.

We all knew what was going on inside.

Five minutes later, they came out. Moishy had the hood of his jacket pulled up over his head so you couldn't see his face. He went over to Chaim and said, "It's settled now?"

"Yup. It's settled," Chaim said.

"Peace from now on?"

"Peace," Chaim said.

And all the boys cheered.

* * *

The story ended just like that. A promise is a promise. But soon after, the rumors began.

What really happened in that classroom? Did Dudi really give Moishy two slaps? Were they hard ones? Maybe they compromised on just one?

A year has gone by since then. The relationship between the two classes improved beyond all recognition. No more fights between one class and another, friendships with kids in the parallel class.

But one truth and one secret hovered over this peace.

Moishy's willingness to absorb the blows and...

what happened in that room. No one knew except Moishy and Dudi, and their lips were sealed.

That's how it all ended, and if I'm disappointing you, I'm sorry, but I think every kid reading this should ask himself what he would like to have happened in that room.

I'm sure most kids would want Dudi to say, "Pinch yourself a little so that your cheek looks red, put your hood on, and act a little weak."

And for those who'd want the two slaps, I suggest you do some thinking about yourself.

What's certain is that anyone who reads this story will at least know how to become a true leader like Moishy.

Glossary

The following glossary provides a partial explanation of some of the Hebrew, Yiddish, and Aramaic words and phrases used in this book. The spellings and definitions reflect the way the specific word is used in this book. There may be alternate spellings and meanings for the words.

aliyah: being called up to say the blessings before and after a Torah reading.

aveilus: mourning.

bachur: yeshivah student.

baruch Hashem: thank G-d.

beis medrash: shul.

berachos: blessings.

b'ezras Hashem: G-d willing.

Birkas Kohanim: the Kohen's Blessing.

Chazal: acronym for *Chachameinu zichronam livrachah*, "Our Sages, may their memory be a blessing."

chesed: kindness.

chevrehman: popular; sociable.

chinuch: education.

chutzpah: insolence.

chutzpadik: acting with *chutzpah*.

derech eretz: acting respectfully and considerately.

emunah: belief.

Gut Shabbos: Good Shabbos.

kapote: elegant long black frock coat worn by Chassidim on Shabbos, holidays, and special occasions.

kippah: yarmulke.

kittel: a special white garment worn on special occasions.

kohen (pl. *kohanim*): direct descendent of Aharon, assigned special privileges and responsibilities, and designated to perform special duties in the Beis HaMikdash.

Kol haolam hazeh gesher tzar meod: This world is [like] a very narrow bridge... (...and the most important thing is not to be afraid).

kugelach: "Five Stones," a game.

lashon kodesh: our holy language.

levayah: funeral.

middos: character traits.

motza'ei Yom Kippur: right after Yom Kippur.

nachas: pleasure; joy.

peah: wig.

peyos: sidelocks.

Pirkei Avos: Ethics of the Fathers.

refuah sheleimah: speedy recovery.

savta: grandmother.

seudah: festive meal.

shtreimel: fur hat worn by Chassidim.

sinas chinam: unfounded hatred.

siyatta diShemaya: Divine providence.

tehillim: psalms.

tovel: immerse into a pool of water for spiritual purity.

Tov L'Hodot LaHashem: It's good to give thanks to Hashem.

vasikin: sunrise.

vatran: one who is willing to give in for the sake of peace.

ym"s: acronym for *yimach shemo*, "may his name be erased."

z"l: acronym for *zichrono l'vrachah*, "may his memory be a blessing.